CW00690372

ROLLS-ROYCE HERI~~TAGE TRUST~~

FROM GIPSY TO GEM
WITH DIVERSIONS
1926 – 1986

Peter Stokes

A History of the de Havilland Aero Engine,
Napier & other associations & of the Rolls-Royce
Small Engine Division/Helicopter Engine Group

HISTORICAL SERIES No 10

Published in 1987 by the
Rolls-Royce Heritage Trust
PO Box 31 Derby England

© 1987 P.R. Stokes

This book, or any parts thereof,
must not be reproduced in any form without the
written permission of the publisher

ISBN 0 9511710 2 X

The Historical Series is published as a joint initiative by the Rolls-Royce Heritage Trust and the Sir Henry Royce Memorial Foundation

Also published in the series:

No 1   Rolls-Royce – the formative years. 1906-1939
       Alec Harvey-Bailey, published by RRHT
No 2   The Merlin in Perspective – the combat years
       Alex Harvey-Bailey, published by RRHT
No 3   Rolls-Royce – the pursuit of excellence
       Alec Harvey-Bailey and Mike Evans, published by HRMF
No 4   In the Beginning – the Manchester origins of Rolls-Royce
       Mike Evans, published by RRHT
No 5   Rolls-Royce – the Derby Bentleys
       Alec Harvey-Bailey, published by HRMF
No 6   The Early Days of Rolls-Royce – and the Montagu Family
       Lord Montagu of Beaulieu, published by RRHT
No 7   Rolls-Royce – Hives, the Quiet Tiger
       Alec Harvey-Bailey, published by HRMF
No 8   Rolls-Royce – Twenty to Wraith
       Alec Harvey-Bailey, published by HRMF
No 9   Rolls-Royce and the Mustang
       David Birch, published by RRHT

Cover: On August 4, 1927, the de Havilland DH71 Tiger Moth monoplane, fitted with the original Gipsy engine and flown by Captain Hubert Broad, established a world speed record of 186.47mph in the light aeroplane (200-350 kg) class.

On August 11, 1986, Westland's G-Lynx fitted with a Gem 60 engine uprated with water methanol injection and modified to produce jet thrust, flown by Trevor Egginton, Chief Test Pilot of Westlands, with Derek Clewes, Flight Test Engineer, established a world speed record for helicopters at 400.87kph/249.10mph breaking by a substantial margin the record previously held by Russia.

Title/end plate: Bob Tanner's drawings of a de Havilland Gipsy Moth and Westland Lynx, de Havilland Comet 1, de Havilland Vampire, Saunders-Roe SR53, Blackburn Buccaneer, Short Sperrin with Gyrons in lower positions, Bristol 188, Westland Wessex, and Sikorsky S70C G-RRTT.

Typesetting by Land & Unwin (Data Sciences) Limited
Printed by B L & U Printing, Wellingborough

CONTENTS

Foreword

de Havilland the Company had *style* and might lay claim, with Rolls-Royce, to the magic of a name. Geoffrey de Havilland the man, whilst quiet and retiring, attracted interest throughout his career. He has been well served by history.

de Havilland was born in 1882, the son of a country parson. His father wrote to The Times of 9 February 1911 as rector of Crux Easton, Hants, with the suggestion concerning the Church of England litany that with the progress of aviation "had not the time arrived for the plea that 'it may please thee to preserve all that travel by land or water' to be amended to add 'or by air'." In his letter he also assumed the omnipotence of The Times "in hoping that the Archbishop of Canterbury, the Pope, and Head of the Greek Church may simultaneously give instruction for that addition to this beautiful form of prayer." He closed his letter "I am afraid I must plead personal interest as being the origin of my suggestion which has arisen owing to my son having taken up aviation and being now at the War Office Balloon Factory, Farnborough."

In 1985 the Prime Minister, Mrs Margaret Thatcher, in addressing the inaugural meeting of the Engineering Assembly and answering a question regarding status said "I wonder why you are so worried about status. I do not think Stephenson, Brunel, de Havilland, Morris, were worried about status. I do not think they needed to be. Status comes from success."

Much has been written on the application of power, not least in the aviation field, but relatively little on powerplants or the people associated with them. de Havilland's aviation career was founded on the design and construction of his own aircraft engine, which was the key to the success of all early flight endeavours. With his success he needed to concentrate on airframe design and gain a dedicated collaborator in the provision of aircraft engines. This he found in Major F B Halford.

History records many beneficial partnerships in arts, science and manufacture; Boulton and Watt to Rolls and Royce, Gilbert and Sullivan to Webber and Rice. It has been remarked, fancifully, that in the DH engine activities the 'H' of the Company's title related to Halford. This is the perspective against which the opening era of this account of what is now the helicopter engine group within Rolls-Royce is set.

Acknowledgements

In bringing this book to print I would acknowledge the help and assistance of Leavesden friends and colleagues from whose experience and endeavours I have drawn assistance and advice. Particularly John Roff and his colleagues in Publications; Photographers working with Peter Scott and John Baumann, and their forebears, who had photographed events and maintained the record. To my colleague Marty Greenhalgh, and to Bob Tanner of Leavesden's Engineering Department whose artistic gift provided my reminiscent aircraft end plates. To Derby colleagues Mike Evans, Chairman of the Rolls-Royce Heritage Trust, in his encouragement from inception of my script and to Peter Kirk's detailed perception and suggestions at finalisation.

Doug Valentine, Chairman, and Roy Matthews, Secretary, of the Leavesden Branch of the Heritage Trust for supporting this endeavour and allowing me the privilege of presenting this history of events to which we and other colleagues, both within and without the Trust branch, have been able to make our various working contributions. I would also acknowledge the enthusiasm of the officers and members of the Watford Industrial History Society who first invited consideration of Leavesden's history and, of course, the forebearance of my wife as I undertook my investigations through past acquisitions of papers, brochures and books and the resultant scribblings at my landing desk, with much tearing and shedding of paper in the night hours personifying me as a worried mouse or rat!

With regard to photographs, I would give a general acknowledgement concerning those photographs copied from various Company publications including in the past the old de Havilland Gazette; also those photographs in the Leavesden archive. I must include also two formal acknowledgements to The Aeroplane Monthly for the drawing of the Heston Napier racer which appeared in 1943 and to Messrs. John Murray for reproduction of Comet photographs first appearing in their publication Comet Highway in 1953. My major acknowlegement must go of course to the succeeding companies employing me through the decades in which they generated continuous motivation in association with products, and the personalities in that particular amalgam of people who make up this aerospace sector of industry.

A particular acknowledgement is to the past and to Dr. Eric Moult who personified the spirit, hopefully reflected in this history, and bridged the generations from the early era to the start of the latter and was to myself and to many colleagues a source of guidance and support, through our training and career stages, and in his latter years a source of encouragement in recording and recognition of the excitement of times past and present. In 1965 towards the end of his career with the company, the preamble to his last major professional paper to the I.Mech.E. "An Engine Designer's Scrapbook" conveyed a mood in regard for things past:-

'Half the marvels of my morning,
Triumph over Time and Space,
Staled by frequence, shrunk by usage,
Into commonest commonplace.'

Tennyson

Bibliography

Aero Engines: Alan E.L. Chorlton. Papers to Royal Society of Arts 1921

Jet Flight: John Grierson. Sampson Low, Marston & Co. Ltd. 1945

Jet Propulsion: Major Frank B. Halford. Paper to the Royal Society of Arts 1946

The Development of the Goblin Engine: E.S. Moult. R.Ae.S.Journal, 1947

The Development of the de Havilland Series of Engines for Light Aircraft: J.L.P. Brodie. Proc. Auto. Div. I. Mech.E., 1950-51

The Aviation Engine: Air Commodore F.R. Banks. Paper to I.Mech.E. 16 Feb. 1951

Civil Aircraft Accident. Report of the Court of Inquiry into the accident to Comet G-ALYP on 10 January 1954 & Comet G-ALYY on 8 April 1954 HMSO 1955

The Development of Reheat: J.L. Edwards. Paper to R.Ae.S. 21 October 1954

Gyroscopic Loading Tests on a Gas-Turbine Rotor: W. Ker Wilson and W.J. Harris. I.Mech.E. 1957

The de Havilland Spectre I: W.N. Neat. R.Ae.S.Journal February 1959

1st Halford Memorial Lecture: J.L.P. Brodie. Paper to R.Ae.S. 4 February 1959

D.H. A History of de Havilland: C. Martin Sharp. Airlife Publishing Ltd. 1982

The design and evolution of an aircraft rocket engine: L.S. Snell. Proc. I.Mech.E. 1963-64.

An Engine Designers Scrapbook: Dr. E.S. Moult. Paper to I.Mech.E. 12 Oct. 1965

British Aviation: The Pioneer Years, Harald Penrose. Cassell 1967 & 1980

de Havilland, The Golden Years 1919-1939. Flight Special 1981

Not much of an Engineer: Sir Stanley Hooker. Airlife 1984

Aerodynamics of the Helicopter World Speed Record: F.J. Perry. Paper to the American Helicopter Society May 1987

Introduction

This volume marks a milestone with the Historical Series. Not only is it the tenth to be published but, more importantly, it is the first to explore a heritage other than that of Rolls-Royce.

Rolls-Royce plc today embraces within its lineage many proud histories of endeavour within the engineering fields of motor car, aero engine and aircraft development and manufacture. All these traditions have contributed to the strengths and capabilities of the Company and all are naturally embraced by the Rolls-Royce Heritage Trust.

"From Gipsy to Gem" covers the de Havilland engine tradition. In writing it, Peter Stokes has displayed courage for he set himself the monumental task of spanning a far-ranging story which began before the first World War and continues through to this day.

Sir Geoffrey de Havilland designed his first aero engine in the years before the first World War for he was among that band of British aviation pioneers which included The Hon C S Rolls, J T C Moore-Brabazon and Blackburn. After the war, in which he distinguished himself as an aircraft designer, he established his own concern and it was this which turned him to the quest for a new breed of small, reliable aero engines to power his new aircraft designs. The book explains how this led de Havilland to seek the help of Major F B Halford, the consultant aero engine designer, and how ultimately the de Havilland range of Gipsy engines was born.

With the second World War came the jet engine and again it was Halford's leadership which created the Goblin and Ghost. However, this volume goes on to describe not only the later engines, but the sites on which the work was carried out, the management and training philosophies of de Havilland and the related products and activities of the engine firm. Rocket engines, racing motor bikes, outboard motors and nuclear engineering all enter the narrative. Lastly, the volume turns to the helicopter gas turbine engine on which the Leavesden site houses the Company's centre of excellence today.

Such a volume could only have been written by an aviation historian practiced in the arts of both research and authorship. Peter Stokes clearly meets these criteria. He has worked for the de Havilland Engine Company and its successors through to Rolls-Royce plc today at the Leavesden factory, where he is now Plant Engineering & Services Manager. As well as being a member of the Rolls-Royce Heritage Trust he also belongs to The Institution of Mechanical Engineers, The Royal Aeronautical Society and The Newcomen Society. In his leisure hours Peter is to be found restoring and maintaining engines of an earlier era. He is involved in restoration at Crofton on the Kennet and Avon Canal which boasts the oldest working steam engines in the World, and at Kew Bridge Steam Museum.

For many this book will give a first opportunity to grasp the extent and significance of the de Havilland aero engine tradition. It brings, at the same time, a new dimension to the Historical Series.

M H EVANS
Chairman

Chapter 1
BEGINNINGS

In 1903 the 21-year-old Geoffrey de Havilland was studying at the Crystal Palace Engineering School and the forward-looking practices of that establishment included an extra term to be devoted to the completion of a personal design-and-make project. For this he selected a motor cycle engine. This was to an advanced specification for its year, of 500cc capacity with mechanically-operated side-valves, detachable cylinder head, and outside flywheel allowing a small, compact crankcase. It scored success both on the road and in hill climbs, and business acumen was demonstrated with the sale of patterns and manufacturing rights. The frame was also designed by de Havilland and from 1903 production continued in a trickle as a 'special' until in 1913, with motor cycling well-established, 'Motor Cycle' was able to announce production of a 500cc machine by Burney and Blackburne Ltd. of Berkhamsted 'until recently known as the de Havilland.'

In 1908 de Havilland decided to build and fly his own aircraft and designed a four cylinder water-cooled horizontally-opposed engine. Cylinders were of 4½in diameter

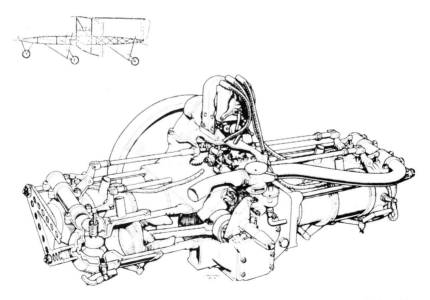

Sectional drawing of the 1909 engine as built to Geoffrey de Havilland's designs by the London based Iris Motor Company.

Geoffrey de Havilland prepares to fly his 1910 aircraft powered by the engine of his own design.

In the Leavesden showroom in November 1961, Sir Geoffrey de Havilland at the ceremonial start up of the replica of his 1909 engine.

with stroke of 4¾in and it was rated at 45hp. The engine had been constructed by the Iris Motor Co. of Willesden and appeared at the Olympia aero show in March 1910 on the Handley Page stand. At least five of the engines were built by Iris as a commercial venture and two of the engines were installed in the Government Balloon Factory's non-rigid airship, the Gamma, replacing an earlier installation of the weighty 80hp Green engine.

Speaking about the engine in 1945, Sir Geoffrey de Havilland said that it "suffered from a fundamental weakness in crankshaft design which resulted in crankshaft failure after a certain number of hours. The engine was of a flat-four type, popular today in light aircraft, but the crankshaft was of two-throw and not the four-throw as in modern engines and the balance was therefore not good."

Publications of that time – 'Aero' and local newspapers – give several references to progress, with a first successful flight reported as being near Newbury in Berkshire on 10 September 1910. This followed an abortive attempt in 1909 by an earlier aircraft which had had novel features, incorporating a Warren-braced fuselage with a forward set of lifting planes and a rearward rudder. Having survived the result of structural failure of this aircraft, de Havilland made his second aircraft more conservative, and generally reminiscent of the Henri Farman biplane. Business sense was once again displayed in that the aircraft was sold to the War Office and Geoffrey de Havilland joined the staff of the Army Balloon Factory at Farnborough in 1910 as designer and test pilot.

From the time he joined the Balloon Factory his energies were directed to the successive aircraft types with which his name is associated, and engine work was undertaken by others. His third design at Farnborough, in 1912, was the BE2 (Bleriot Experimental 2) and this aircraft, powered by a 70hp Renault engine – and the first to be inherently stable – was a pointer to developments in the years ahead. In 1914 he joined the newly-formed Aircraft Manufacturing Company and though he was commissioned as Lieutenant on the outbreak of the war and joined an RFC squadron he was sent back to industry to complete the design of the DH1 observation aircraft. This was powered by a Renault engine of 90hp, later to be replaced by a 120hp Beardmore engine developed from licenced production of a 'similar' Austro-Daimler engine.

In 1916 the most noteworthy and prolific of the DH first war designs, the DH4, was built and subsequently developed as the DH9 from 1917. Prime powerplant of

A 1917 DH9 daylight bombing aircraft with its B H P/Puma engine.

11

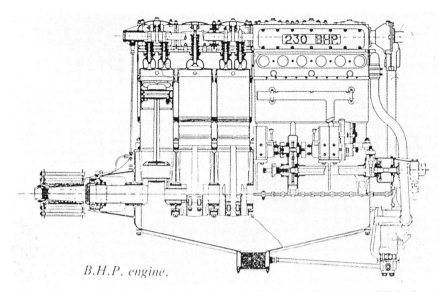

B.H.P. engine.

Sectional elevation of the 230hp B H P engine subsequently developed as the Armstrong Siddeley Puma.

this aircraft in the war years was an engine developed from the later 160hp Beardmore type, the 230hp BHP engine. This was in turn developed by the Coventry company Armstrong Siddeley as the Puma and founded that company's aircraft engine activities. The BHP engine and the Puma represented a major production programme for service in the 1914-18 war with 3,200 built at a unit cost of £1,089.

The point of emphasis on the BHP in this particular narrative relates to the 'H' in the collaboration of Beardmore, Halford and Pullinger. T C Pullinger was head of Arrol Johnston at Dumfries to whom the Royal Aircraft Factory let the contract for development. F B Halford in 1915 was a 21-year-old member of the Air Ministry Inspection Department. After education at Felstead School he had learnt to fly and was a Pilot Instructor at the age of 19 and subsequently became an AID engine examiner. He joined the RFC at the outbreak of war and served in France as a Foreman Artificer and was then commissioned Second Lieutenant and re-appointed to the AID.

Thus in 1916 began one of history's collaborations of two like-minded men with complementing personalities. de Havilland, whose life was dedicated to aircraft development and reflected a particular skill in engine integration, and Frank Halford, whose engine design skills were always rooted in aircraft requirements.

During the immediate post-war period Captain de Havilland and Major Halford found themselves specialists in a virtually unwanted industry. With aircraft there was interest in civil applications and the initiation of airlines, but only with the adaptation of the large stocks of ex-military aircraft and engines.

de Havilland was engaged in this work, continuing in employment with the company now dubbed 'Airco'. Halford in the latter years of the war had undertaken work on engine supercharging with Harry Ricardo, regarded then as the high priest of the internal combustion engine, and now followed up this association as a partner

Major Halford sitting centre right of Major Bulman with other officers of the Aeronautical Inspection Department in 1918. G.P. Bulman as a lifelong associate of F B Halford was his immediate predecessor in the latters 1951-52 presidency of the Royal Aeronautical Society.

with the formation of H Ricardo Ltd. Initially Halford pursued sleeve-valve patent applications in the USA and subsequently the practical development of the Ricardo Triumph motorcycle, securing class records and competing in the 1921 TT. In 1923 he set up in private practice as a design consultant with an office in North Kensington, assisted by John Brodie, a colleague of the Arrol Johnston-BHP days, and an outcome was the 1½ litre supercharged 'Halford Special' of 1924 which competed at Brooklands.

In 1924 Halford shifted his office and activities to Croydon as consultant to the Aircraft Disposal Company in support of their plans for the adaptation and disposal of considerable stocks of ex-wartime engines, with particular emphasis on quantities of the 80hp Renault V8 engine.

de Havilland found that his employment with Airco was to be terminated as a consequence of the fact that whilst Birmingham Small Arms Ltd. (BSA) had optimistically acquired the company in 1920, they then decided to go out of the aviation business. de Havilland, with his colleagues, sought finance to start his own company and was fortunate to find a backer in Mr Holt Thomas, previously of Airco, who had now formed Air Transport & Travel Ltd. operating adapted DH aircraft. BSA let the team take their designs with them. Consequently, the de Havilland Aircraft Company Ltd. was formed on 25 September 1920, at Stag Lane Aerodrome, Edgware, ten eventful years after the flight of its founder's first aircraft. Initially work was on adaptations of the DH9 series to various civilian roles, followed by a wide range of types through the early 1920s – passenger aircraft, bombers and fighter

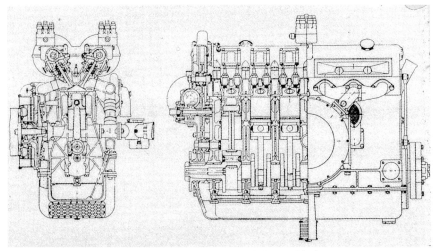

1½ litre turbo-supercharged engine of the 1924 'Halford Special' Aston Martin.

reconnaissance aircraft – all relatively large and powerful with ex-wartime engines of 300-600hp from Rolls-Royce and Armstrong Siddeley, the predominant contemporary engine manufacturers.

With the intention of encouraging private flying and general air-mindedness the Air Ministry sponsored a competition for light aircraft in 1923. The emphasis was on light and diminutive construction with engines to be adapted motor cycle types limited to a maximum of 750cc. de Havilland built the DH53 as a contender. A number of different powerplants were fitted, amongst them being the 26hp Blackburne Tom-Tit, doubtless as a result of earlier associations. This engine drove its propeller at 3,000rpm and the resulting note in flight led to the aircraft being dubbed Humming Bird. Fifteen of these aircraft were built, ten of them for the Air Ministry, and although the competition did not produce the looked-for light aircraft movement, the DH53 did useful work in the investigations into the launching of aircraft from beneath airships, undertaken from the R33.

The DH51 flew in 1924, adopting an opposite policy aimed at providing the private flyer with a large aircraft able to carry three people for touring. The engine fitted was a 120hp adaptation by the Aircraft Disposal Co. of the government surplus 80hp Renault engines, fitted with modern aluminium cylinder heads as a result of Halford's initiative. Only three DH51 aircraft were built, as again the concept did not satisfy market requirements. An example of both the DH51 and DH53 still exist today at the Shuttleworth Aircraft Collection in Bedfordshire.

In 1925, with the first flight of the DH60 Moth, the right formula was found for the private owner, for both touring and training aircraft. The aircraft was a two-thirds scale of the DH51 and the engine requirement was likewise reduced to 60hp and satisfied by the simple expedient of literally halving the 120hp Airdisco engine. de Havilland and Halford consulted and physically laid out the engine components on a work bench, discarding four of the cylinders and designing a new crankcase and shaft. The resulting engine was named 'Cirrus' and powered all the early Moths. In

14

Cirrus engine in the DH60 Moth circa 1926.

Cirrus Moth instruction with admiring host of ladies, the chorus from the production of "The Good Companions".

15

subsequent years, with the demise of the Airdisco company, this engine design continued in manufacture by the Hermes Engineering Co., and eventually, from 1934, by Blackburn Aircraft as the 'Cloud' series of engines in competition with the DH types.

By the following year the success of the Moth was assured as orders flooded in from flying clubs and private owners. Cobham flew to Zurich and back in a day and the Kings Cup Air Race was won by a Moth. On the basis of this success, and the need for expansion, de Havilland decided to ensure engine supply and development by the manufacture of an alternative but similar engine. Halford, in his freelance design capacity, was asked to design a new engine for the DH Aircraft Co. without the constraints of the adaption of war-time parts. Power could be increased and weight reduced.

Chapter 2
THE GIPSY ERA

The Gipsy

Design commenced on 29 October 1926, and the engine was running by mid-1927. With exuberance in the success of the Company, a new aircraft was designed, matched to the expected potential of the new engine. The engine was named 'Gipsy', had a bore of 114mm, stroke of 128mm and, with a compression ratio of 5.5, produced 135hp at 2,850rpm. The aircraft was designed specifically as a racing aircraft, a monoplane with its single-seat fuselage literally tailored to the moderate size of the then chief test pilot, Hubert Broad. On August 27th the aircraft, the DH71 Tiger Moth, broke the light aeroplane speed record for the 100km closed circuit at 186.5mph, at that time faster than contemporary fighters.

The engine was subsequently produced for the Moth. Rating was reduced to a maximum of 100hp at 2,100rpm and normal operation of 85hp at 1,900rpm. Compression ratio was 5.0 and the valve gear modified with smaller and more practical vertical valves. As a consequence of this reversal of normal development practice,

Early ground running with the monoplane Tiger Moth in 1927. Test Pilot Hubert Broad alongside the cock-pit throttling the engine.

The 1927 Gipsy I engine.

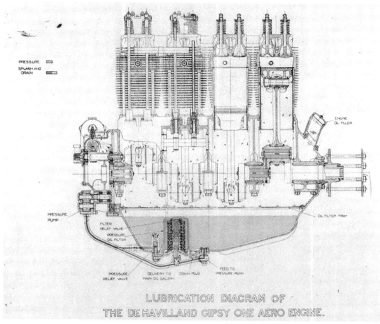

Gipsy I section. Simplicity for reliability.

1928 Gipsy Moth flown by Sir Geoffrey de Havilland. Publicity proving with sealed engine for 600hrs of flight.

Aerial view of Stag Lane in the late '20s with Moths much in evidence.

19

The abortive 200hp 'Ghost' engine powering the prototype Hawk Moth in 1928.

i.e. downrating rather than uprating, the seal was set on the Gipsy engine's prime feature, reliability, and the near-traditional assumption of overhaul at 200 hours was broken. 600 hour operations of sealed engines was demonstrated in the first production year. In this year the team, led by Frank Halford, still an independent consultant and now based in Victoria Street, London, was joined by Eric Moult who in later years was to succeed him as Technical Director of the de Havilland Engine Co.

The Gipsy engine flew in the Moth in July 1928 and thus alternatives could be specified, with rivalry between Cirrus and Gipsy Moths. In 1929 the Gipsy II was introduced, uprated to 120hp with a stroke increased to 140mm, improved cooling and enclosed valve gear. Thus the Gipsy became the prime powerplant.

Francis Chichester flew his Gipsy Moth to Australia in seventeen days and founded his solo navigating career which culminated in the 1960 transatlantic sailing race. It is a nice twist of history that the yacht Gipsy Moth III, a proud item of maritime history preserved at Greenwich, bears its name as a consequence of Sir Geoffrey de Havilland's policy of naming his products in association with his hobby of winged nature and lepidoptery.

In 1930 Amy Johnson made her epic flight from England to Australia in a second-hand Moth, purchased for £600. She was, of course, a remarkably determined young woman and the flight was the means of establishing herself as a professional aviator. It was the culmination of two years of work under de Havilland tutelage. She flew with the London Aeroplane Club at Stag Lane and qualified as a ground engineer on both airframes and engines and was thus licenced in all aspects of the Gipsy Moth's operational requirements. In the nineteen days which elapsed in her flight a broken propeller was replaced, damaged undercarriage repaired, sundry wing ribs rebuilt and a complete upper wing replaced. Minimal work was required on the engine. 'Jason' and its engine are preserved in the Science Museum in London, as are examples of most of the Gipsy engine range.

Something of an oddity in 1929 was the construction of the Ghost engine which reverted back to the Renault/Airdisco configuration of an 8-cylinder 'Vee'. This engine, of 200hp, was applied to the DH75 Hawk Moth, another design which failed to find a market. The DH80 Puss Moth followed in 1930, an aircraft of similar configuration which was an immediate success as something of a sports car of the air accommodating two in tandem, with the rear seat large enough for an occasional extra passenger.

Contributing to this success was the Gipsy III engine, the first of the inverted Gipsy engines. Benefits sought from this change of configuration were primarily a better thrust-line for the airscrew and improved view for the pilot, together with more convenient exhaust disposal. Prime problem was the need to substitute a dry sump system with scavenge pumps for the previous simple automotive-type wet sump arrangement. In turn, however, the inverted flight and aerobatic capabilities of the engine were ensured. All the four-cylinder Gipsies produced up to the fifties featured a redundant cast boss at the underside front of the crankcase to accommodate an oil filler cap not required since the twenties!

A further version of the Moth was flown in 1931, the Moth Major, and this proved the breakthrough in attracting a service order from the Royal Air Force as the Tiger Moth. The name 'Major' transferred to the engine as giving it a suitably military standing. Power was at 130hp with slight changes in bore to 118 mm, compression ratio to 5.25 and running speed to 2350 rpm. At this rating the engine powered the 8,800 Tiger Moths which were built to meet the requirements, in conjunction with the similarly-powered Miles Magister, of the wartime Empire Air Training programme. A total of 14,615 Gipsy Majors were built.

Through the '30s the four-cylinder Gipsies, in competition with the Blackburn Cirrus range, powered the private and light transport aircraft of virtually all the British aircraft manufacturers, among them Miles, Percival and Fairey.

The Gipsy Six

In 1933 a positive need was identified for an engine of 200hp to power the emergent light transport aircraft market. A six-cylinder edition of the Major was produced with the standard cylinder of 118mm bore and 140mm stroke and 5.25 compression ratio. First application was the four-engined DH86 and subsequently the twin-engined DH89 Dragon Rapide which was developed for service use as the Dominie.

In common with most six-throw crankshaft engines, torsional vibration problems were expected, duly confirmed and fortunately, with the assistance of the Royal Aircraft Establishment (RAE), quickly eradicated. The solution lay in a novel firing order, 1-2-4-6-5-3, necessitating a rather tortuous overlaying inlet manifold configuration for the twin-carburettor system.

In 1934 entries were invited for the Melbourne Centenary Air Race, England to Australia, competing for the MacRobertson Trophy. Initially this appeared to be an event mismatched to any British participation and tailor-made for American and Dutch interests with the introduction by KLM of the Douglas DC2 for East Indies service. The de Havilland Aircraft Co. decided to speculate and published an advertisement in the trade press offering to build a competitive aircraft. With interest

Painting of the 1934 comet G-ACSS with group including Halford in discussion (1954 memento for 20 year club).

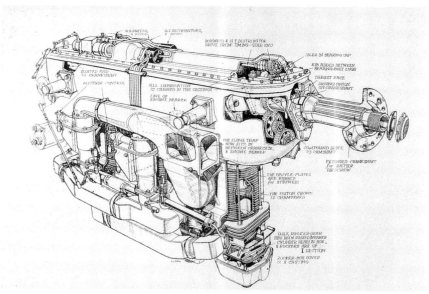

Gipsy Six racing engine for the 1934 England/Australia race showing the modifications from the basic 6 cylinder engine.

confirmed and finance inferred, the project emerged as a combination of the airframe innovations of the era, matched to a minimum drag, maximum fuel capacity aeroplane with a crew of two to minimise transit stops. The resultant DH88 Comet incorporated, as the first British aircraft to do so, the combination of wing flaps, retractable undercarriage and variable-pitch (VP) propellers.

Engine contribution was met by an uprating of the Gipsy Six as the 'R' with an increase of compression ratio to 6.5 giving 225hp at 2,400rpm for take-off. The biggest gain, however, was the power match to both take-off and cruise cases provided by the variable-pitch propellers. After take-off in fine pitch, with the propellers changed to coarse pitch, the engines could cruise at 2,250rpm full throttle at 10,000ft. thus giving 60% more power than that which would have been available for a fixed-pitch take-off/cruise combination.

The problem, however, was in the state of variable-pitch propeller design at that time. Whilst the provision of American-designed fully-variable propellers was considered, these presented supply and installation problems. As a consequence French Ratier units of truly Gallic ingenuity were adopted. The design assumed a normal operational mode in coarse pitch. For the take-off case in fine pitch a rubber 'sac' in the propeller hub was inflated to press on a piston and, through a pitch change mechanism, maintain the pitch setting. When flight speed built up to approximately 150mph the drag on a small circular plate forward of the hub was transmitted to a tyre-type valve which deflated the 'sac'! Fine pitch could only be regained after landing by re-inflation with a bicycle pump.

Three Comet aircraft took part in the race and G-ACSS flown by G W A Scott and T Campbell Black won the event, covering 11,700 miles in an elapsed time of 70 hours 54 minutes with six intermediate stops.

In the years up to the second world war the Comets made many record breaking flights, those of G-ACSS continuing to be the most publicised. Engines reverted to standard ratings and were fitted with Hamilton Standard hydromatic propellers then being marketed by DH as the foundation of their propeller business.

Ground runs on the Mollisons Comet G-ACSP, probably at Mildenhall. Note Ratier propellers with drag plates on spinners.

The beautiful DH Gipsy Twelve powered Albatross type airliner in 1938 service with Imperial Airways 'Frobisher'.

F B Halford in the 1930s.

24

The Gipsy Twelve & a brief Napier diversion

Within three weeks of the success of the Australia race DH made submissions to Air Ministry for support in the development of a transport aircraft of similar clean lines to the Comet racers. No market existed at that time, however, but the subject was pursued and in January 1936 a contract was obtained for two experimental long-range transport aircraft to carry a load of 1,000lb for 2,500 miles against continuous 40mph headwinds. This requirement emerged as the DH91 Albatross airliner which flew on 20 May 1937, powered by four Gipsy Twelve supercharged engines of 525hp each.

To appreciate the genesis of this engine it is necessary to consider the relationship between the Engine Department of the de Havilland Aircraft Company, which was primarily a manufacturing organization, and the design organization of Major Halford which continued as an independent consultancy serving a number of organizations, though primarily de Havilland and Napier.

The premises of D Napier & Son Ltd. were at Acton in West London, and the market they sought to serve was biased towards higher power requirements and military service. In the 1920s they were in strong competition with Bristol's Jupiter, Armstrong Siddeley's Jaguar and the re-emergent Rolls-Royce with its Kestrel and Buzzard engines. The premier Napier engine was the 500hp water-cooled Lion. At the end of the 1920s their fortunes were in decline and two parallel lines of development were pursued. A licence was taken for the development of the German Junkers Jumo opposed-piston diesel engines and Halford's organization was engaged for the design and development of compact, low frontal area, supercharged and high-revving air-cooled engines to contest the competitors' lower rotational speed air- and water-cooled engines.

The Napier Rapier 16-cylinder 'H' engine of 350hp ran in 1929 and could be

The 1929 DH77 Interceptor fighter prototype with its Napier Rapier engine.

Halford's first H type engine for Napiers in 1929, the 350hp 16 cylinder Rapier.

considered conceptually as combining four Gipsy engines on a common crankcase although using smaller cylinders and gearing down from 3,500rpm. Centrifugal supercharging was introduced. Initial application of this engine was for the DH77 monoplane interceptor, a scaled-up edition of the prototype Gipsy-powered DH71 Tiger Moth. The aeroplane was of similar performance, achieving 182mph, much in advance of contemporary fighters, but did not attract any orders. Subsequent applications of the engine included the Short Mercury, the upper component of the 'Maia' composite transatlantic aeroplane, and the Fairey Seafox, the Royal Navy's spotter aircraft in the Graf Spee action.

In 1934 the 24-cylinder Dagger engine of 675hp ran. The date suggests related thinking to the Gipsy Six engines as four banks of six. Most interesting potential application of this engine was the Martin Baker MB2 fighter. It also powered the Hawker Hector army co-operation aircraft and the Handley Page Hereford bomber, both of which were somewhat outmoded at the commencement of 1939-45 war.

The Mayo composite aircraft, Mercury the upper component with its four Rapier engines.

The 24 cylinder Dagger engine, power plant of the Hawker Hector and Henley and the Handley Page Hereford. Designed in 1934, initially at 675hp, it was the first engine to utilise hydraulic tappets.

The Gipsy 12 brought together features of Halford's former designs for both DH and Napier. In perpetuation of the Gipsy range its two cylinder banks of six, with the common 118mm bore, 140mm stroke, and 6.0 compression rate, were inverted at 60 degrees giving the compact configuration favoured by the contemporary German engines. The engine was the first DH unit to be supercharged and the geared propeller drive had been predated only by the unsuccessful Ghost. The prime feature, however, was the air cooling configuration with the engine tightly cowled. Duct work took air from the wing leading edge, maximising flow from the propellers during ground running and achieving maximum ram in flight, and directed this air forward round the cylinders to exhaust rearwards with the cylinder exhaust and thus offering a possible net gain in thrust.

Development of both the Albatross and its engines was cut short by the war but its efficiency index of 33.3 gross ton-miles-per-gallon was higher than for any other transport aircraft. Seven were built and they continued to be operational in the war years. A rather less memorable aircraft using the same engine configuration was the DH93 Don, a single-engine communications type of which approximately 50 were built.

The Gipsy Minor

July 1937 saw the first flight of the DH94 Moth Minor, a small monoplane of similar concept to the post-war Chipmunk but intended as a basic club machine at minimal cost – £575 ex-works. To match this, a new engine, the Gipsy Minor, rated at 90hp and designed for ease of production, was introduced. Features included diminutive size at two-thirds the weight of current four-cylinder engines, a single dual-output magneto, and the incorporation of the main bearing caps in the crankcase cover. The war intervened before production got underway and in 1940 all parts and drawings were shipped to Australia where approximately 100 aircraft were built to participate in training programmes.

Hawker Hector with Napier Dagger.

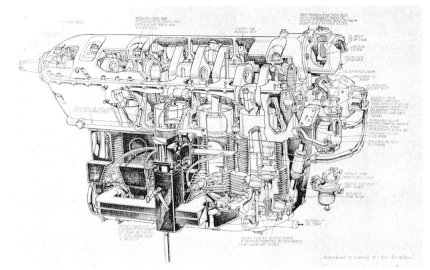

Gipsy Minor in section.

Gipsy Minors on production assembly at Stag Lane in 1939 prior to the war cutting short prospects for mass production.

Chapter 3
THE 1939 – 1945 WAR

The Gipsies

In the period of the war years there was little innovation in the Gipsy range of engines. They offered tried and proven performance as required for the training programmes in the expansion of the RAF through the Empire Air Training Scheme, and for communications aircraft.

One wartime development in 1940 was the adaptation of the Gipsy Six engine as an airborne auxiliary powerplant specifically to provide electrical power for the Wellington bomber aircraft equipped to explode German magnetic mines from the air. The aircraft carried a large magnetic coil with a diameter of approximately two-thirds wing span, which simulated the magnetic field of a ship, detonating the mine to the rear of the aircraft as it flew over at wave top height. The engine drove a 135kW trolleybus motor adapted as a generator and the whole set was mounted in the aircraft bomb bay with cooling air ducted from the aircraft wing root leading edge in the manner of the Albatross. Seventeen sets of this equipment were built and particular operations were associated with the Suez Canal where five aircraft were based through the critical war years. It was claimed that one aircraft could sweep the Canal in 22 minutes.

Also in 1941 a four-cylinder auxiliary power unit of 60hp was designed specifically to meet the requirements of the large Short Shetland flying boat, but production was not undertaken.

Wartime production of Gipsy engines in the UK was of 10,212 engines, made up of 7,795 Gipsy Majors, 1,264 Gipsy Queens for fixed-pitch propellers and 1,153 Gipsy Queens for variable-pitch propellers. The Gipsy Engine Repair Department overhauled 3,387 Gipsies and guided the activities of daughter firms on overhaul: Blackburn 1,193 Gipsies, Wrightways 1,990, Scottish Aviation 450, Pobjoy 220. In Australia, drawings of the Gipsy Major 1 engine, which in European usage had always been in metric as a throwback to its 1914-18 Renault antecedents, were anglicised in 1940 and subsequently 1300 'inch-unit' engines were produced!

Another wartime activity of the DH Aircraft Co's engine department was the overhaul of the Rolls-Royce Merlin, the pre-eminent front-line engine of the war years. Within six weeks of the programme commencing in 1940 an output of 10 overhauls a week was achieved and in the 16 weeks to September 15th, the height of the Battle of Britain, 152 Merlins were returned to service. Overhauls continued until late 1944 with a total of 9,022 in all, an average of 38 per week for 4½ years.

Halford, Napier & the Sabre

A further reference to Halford's association with Napier needs to be made concerning what must be regarded as the pinnacle of his career with the piston engine. In

May 1935 he became Technical Director of Napier whilst continuing in his consultancy role with the de Havilland Aircraft Co. In that year Napiers initiated a design study for a 24 cylinder horizontal 'H' configuration twin-crankshaft, sleeve-valve, liquid-cooled military engine of 36.65 litres capacity to utilise 100 octane fuel. It evolved from an earlier study for a diesel unit. Its major feature to ensure high specific power was for operation at high rotational speed, 4,000rpm.

As a 2000hp. proposal it was written into Air Ministry fighter specification F18/37 calling for a 20% improvement in performance over the Hawker Hurricane and in March 1937 Sydney Camm produced a preliminary design for the Hawker Type N, a 12-gun fighter. On 23 November 1937 the Napier-Halford E107 ran and was named 'Sabre'. In January 1938 the engine passed initial acceptance tests at 1350hp and in

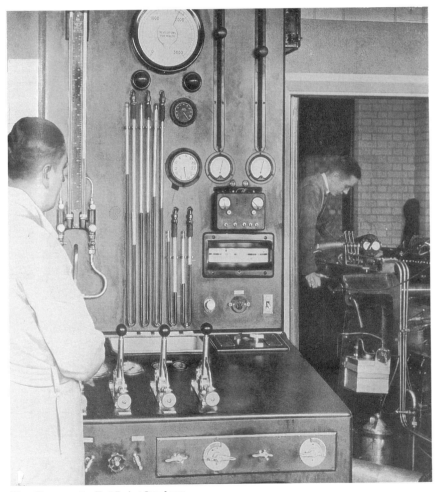

Gipsy Dynamometer Test Bed at Stag Lane.

August of that year Hawker Aircraft received contracts for construction of four prototypes, two Type N with the Sabre and two Type R, alternatively-powered by the Rolls-Royce Vulture.

With the Sabre launched and prototypes Air Ministry funded, Napier launched a plan to accelerate development of the engine in association with an attempt to regain the World Absolute Speed Record, raised in 1938 to 468.94mph for Germany by the Messerschmitt Bf109R. A E Hagg, formerly of de Havilland Aircraft from 1921, designer of the Comet and Albatross, had resigned in 1937 and was in employment with Napier. By December 1938 he had prepared basic layouts of an all-wood, low-wing racer. Lord Nuffield backed the project and Heston Aircraft Ltd., formerly Comper, were contracted to build two Sabre-powered aircraft, the Nuffield-Napier-Heston Racers.

In early 1939 clearance tests were undertaken on a ground level rated version of the Sabre to clear it for five minutes full throttle operation, giving a power of 2560hp at 4000rpm and 9.2lb boost. With the outbreak of war the first aircraft, G-AFOK, was virtually complete and the decision was taken to proceed with this but to defer further construction of the second aeroplane. On 12th March 1940 the racer undertook its taxiing trials and then on 12th June it undertook its first and only flight piloted by Squadron Leader G L G Richmond of the Heston Aircraft Company. The seven-minute flight ended in disaster with the aircraft stalling in the last stages of the approach and crash landing, but the pilot survived. He explained afterwards that:

> "The elevator control, which had been satisfactory during taxi-ing trials, was again adequately effective up to the point when the aeroplane became airborne, from this point on, the elevators ceased to be powerful enough to overcome the fore-and-aft control which appeared to be exercised by the varying airflow caused by engine revolutions. In other words: irrespective of the position of the control column, a decrease of r.p.m. caused the nose to fall, and an increase lifted the nose to the horizon. This was discovered just after take-off, when the aeroplane had been thrown into the air a trifle prematurely by some irregularity of the ground with the nose rather higher in the air than desired. It was immediately found that the use of the elevator would not lower the nose on the horizon. This was so marked that the undercarriage was not retracted, as it was felt that the drag of the wheels below the wing was probably preventing the angle of climb being steeper.
>
> It was then that one discovered (about 30 seconds after take-off) that the engine coolant had reached its maximum permissible temperature and was still rising. This prevented an interesting flight from being protracted, the next valuable few minutes being almost entirely taken up in manoeuvring for position to approach to land, and the unfortunate finale spoiled the chances of obtaining more data.
>
> There is thus a special reason for hope that the second aeroplane may be completed and flown so that the cause of this peculiarity may be definitely attributed to either the incorrect positioning of the tailplane or to the disturbance caused by the relation of the open cooling duct vent to the elevators."

With the war entering its most critical phase no further work was undertaken and both aircraft were eventually broken up.

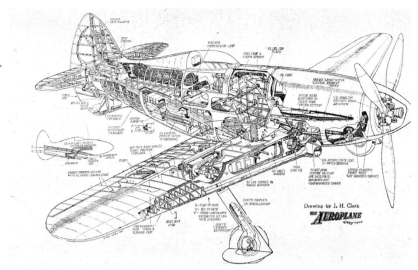

The Heston Napier racer with its Sabre engine in 1940.

The first Sabre for installation in the prototype Typhoon was delivered to Hawker Aircraft Limited on 30 December 1939 and on 24 February 1940 the aircraft undertook its first flight piloted by Philip G Lucas who was awarded the George Medal, at a later date, for landing this prototype aeroplane after severe buffeting started to tear away the stressed skin wing root covering. Testing continued but with the war situation plans for immediate production were shelved. In June, the Sabre Series I passed the Air Ministry 100-hour type test at a max. power of 2060hp at 3,700rpm and a boost of 7lb. Flight development of the engine continued in two Fairey Battle aircraft, and production was re-initiated. In July 1941 deliveries of the Typhoon Mark 1A to the Royal Air Force commenced, and this aircraft was the RAF's first 400mph fighter. In September 1941 the Duxford Wing of Nos. 56 and 609 Fighter Squadrons exchanged their Spitfire for cannon-armed Typhoon Mark 1Bs. From 1941 to 1944, 3,330 Typhoons were delivered to the Royal Air Force.

As a consequence of this pace of development to meet the exigency of war, problems arose with both airframe and engine although early engine development phases had been remarkably trouble-free. Airframe problems required a programme of strengthening rear fuselages. The engine problems centred on the sleeve-valve arrangements.

Halford's early experience with Ricardo coincided with their work on sleeve-valves. These had been developed to the Burt McCullum patents and applied to the Argyll 6-cylinder aero engine which won a 1914 Air Ministry competition although it did not enter production. Post-war, and following Ricardo's work, Roy Fedden of Bristol Aeroplane's Engine Department took up the challenge of the sleeve-valve and his engine series evolved into the Hercules, the predominant British radial engine of the war years. The 4-port sleeve-valve configuration was that adopted for the Sabre and later to the Rolls-Royce Eagle of the early post-war years which developed the Sabre configuration.

33

Napiers were unsuccessful in finding a cure to the wear and deterioration of their chrome molybdenum sleeves and in 1943 the Ministry of Aircraft Production insisted on collaboration between Bristol and Napier in adaptation of the Bristol-developed sleeve material in nitrided austenitic steel and the machining technique to establish the necessary roundness and integrity. A step change in serviceability was established with Bristol-manufactured sleeves and Napier's Liverpool and Acton factories then installed the necessary production machinery to allow the massive support needed to restore the engine programme.

In September 1941 Hawker Aircraft commenced design work on a thin wing version of the Typhoon to take advantage of promised increases in power and overcome compressibility problems in high speed dives. In November 1941 the Air Ministry placed an order for two prototypes of aircraft designated the Typhoon Mk. II; one to be powered by the production Sabre II and another by a major new development variant, the Sabre Series IV. This aircraft, re-designated as the Tempest F Mk.I, flew on 24 February 1943 powered by the Sabre IV rated at 2240hp at 4,000rpm at an altitude rating of 8,000ft and with 9lb boost. The major change in this engine was the substitution of R.A.E.-Hobson fuel injection for the former S.U. suction carburettors. This arrangement had the benefits of removal of chokes to maximise airflow, minimise gravitational effects (and therefore limitations in associated flight manoeuvres), reduce weight and improve fuel consumption.

The Tempest entered service with the Royal Air Force in April 1944, joining the Typhoon in its ground attack role, and subsequently, with its high power and speed, became pre-eminent in low level combat and in contesting the V1 flying bombs. The outstanding type was probably the Tempest Mk.V Series II which was fitted with the Sabre IIB carburettor engine giving 2420hp at 3,850rpm, rated at sea level and with

Sabre powered Tempests 'scramble' from Volkel, Holland, in March 1945.

34

11lb boost. In 1944 one of these achieved a maximum speed of 435mph at 17,000ft and 392mph at sea level. Range was 820 miles at 5,000ft increasing to 1300 miles with long range tanks.

The injection version of the engine had reverted to a lower priority after the flight of the prototype but on 9 May 1944 the Tempest Mk.VI flew with the Sabre V engine rated at 2,600hp at 3,850rpm with boost increased to 15lb. Associated with the boost uprating was a complete supercharger and induction configuration re-design, substituting a single-sided impeller for the previous double-sided unit which, with its direct entry with injection arrangements, provided enhanced flow and higher boost pressures.

At the end of the war all Royal Air Force Typhoons were withdrawn from service whilst the Tempest, 800 of which had been built, remained in service into the 1950s with the Sabre engine developed to the Mk.VII variant. This, with water methanol injection and 17lb boost, was rated at 3,000hp for take-off and 2,760hp at 12,500ft with a fuel consumption at .84lbs per hour per hp. The Sabre was, throughout these latter war years, the most powerful piston engine in use, and overall the most powerful piston engine to be used in Royal Air Force service.

In 1943 Napier was taken over by English Electric with a change of management. F.B. Halford continued in charge of design until he relinquished this responsibility when he became Chairman and Technical Director of the de Havilland Engine Company upon its formation in 1944.

Side elevation of a Mark 5 Napier Sabre with injector carburettor and single sided supercharger impeller.

Tempest and Typhoon displayed in the Royal Air Force Museum flanking the 24 cylinder Napier Sabre engine.

Chapter 4
THE DE HAVILLAND ENGINE COMPANY

The Company

The history of the de Havilland piston engine activities discussed to this point took place at the Stag Lane, Edgware, works of the company. Until 1930 work on both airframes and engines was at Stag Lane but with the encroachment of suburbia the de Havilland Aircraft Company looked for new aerodrome premises to allow continuing development and flying activities. The Hatfield site was selected and initially the Flying Training School transferred. Over the subsequent years, all airframe activities were transferred to Hatfield and the last flight from Stag Lane aerodrome was in 1934, with the house builders ready to pounce on the remains of the aerodrome. Subsequent to that date, the factory concentrated on engine and propeller work and then, in the latter years, solely on engine work and laboratory support for the group of companies that then emerged.

In February, 1944, the de Havilland Engine Company Ltd was formed at Stag

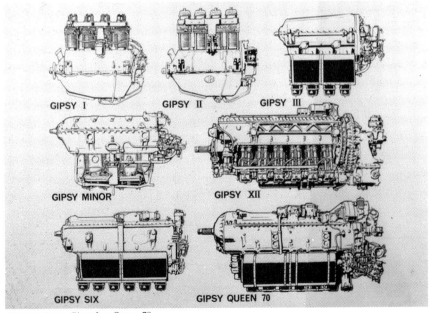

Gipsy variants, Gipsy I to Queen 70.

Lane from the Engine Division of the de Havilland Aircraft Company. In 1945 the Government leased the aircraft factory at Leavesden to the de Havilland Engine Company and in 1946 the Gipsy production division moved to the Leavesden No. 1 factory, previously operated by London Aircraft Production Group for Handley Page Halifax bomber production. Mosquito activity at the No. 2 factory was then phased out in favour of sheet metal fabrication for engine requirements.

In this era the emphasis of the newly-formed Engine Company swung to the jet propulsion engine, in which field the Company found itself in a strong international position as a result of pioneering wartime efforts. Development of piston engines was at low priority with decreasing market opportunities, and the general influence of the gas turbine raised expectation that even the smaller piston engine applications would succumb. In 1946 a turboprop gas turbine engine, designated the H3 and designed to give 450hp, was run. This was expected to replace piston engines in such airframes as the Dove, with the related assumption that the airframes be pressurised and operate at higher altitudes. In the event, the development contract for this particular engine was terminated early as were contracts for other small gas turbines at Bristol and Napier. Subsequent development of gas turbines has still not ousted piston engines from lower power applications due to the general cost and complexity of the gas turbine and inability to achieve competitive fuel consumptions in this power range. Gipsy engine development and production continued, however, in meeting the market potential until United Kingdom airframe involvement waned in the face of American competition.

Gipsy Major

The Gipsy Major engine emerged from the war years with a new lease of life as the Major 10 and production concentrated on the Mk.2 edition giving 145hp. Generally

Gipsy powered Kings Cup winners.

38

similar to the pre-war engines, it incorporated relatively minor modifications, such as sodium-cooled exhaust valves to meet the necessity of running on 80 octane petrol. Other features substituted for the previous taper shaft and key a splined propeller shaft, necessitated by revised propeller designs, and fitted accessories matched to the electrical and instrumentation requirements of post-war aeroplanes. The engine found a number of applications, the most successful being in the DHC-1 Chipmunk two-seat trainer.

Queen 70 & Queen 30

All the post-war 6-cylinder engines were now designated as 'Queens' although in earlier years, the designation 'Queen' had applied purely to the military application of the engine. In 1944 a new Gipsy Queen, designated as the 70 and rated at 350hp, was run. This incorporated, in addition to supercharging, a geared propeller drive system. This engine found very positive market applications, as did the simpler unsupercharged Queen 30 which ran in 1945 giving 240hp.

The Queen 70 found its main application in the de Havilland Dove twin-engined light airliner. With the expected de Havilland panache, the Dove took to the air in September, 1945, heralding the post-war era as the first of the concepts emerging from the Brabazon Committee which had planned British civil airliner developments in the post-war years.

This 6-cylinder engine was of 120mm bore and 150mm stroke with moderate degree of supercharge at 6lb and a compression ratio of 6.5. It incorporated an

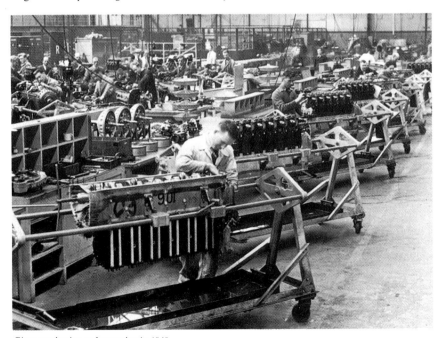

Gipsy production at Leavesden in 1948.

39

injection carburettor, capitalizing on Hobson's wartime development work, and another feature, derived from Sabre work, was the supercharger drive arrangement of a long torsion shaft running from the front of the engine inside the camshaft. Other features of the engine were aimed at eliminating torsional vibration problems and, as such, reflected something of the nature of art-over-science in combatting the inbred problems of a 6-cylinder in-line design.

The 6-throw crankshaft initially incorporated pendulum-type vibration dampers which were subsequently locked and thus reverted to balance weights. The main feature was the incorporation of a 'Bibby' spring coupling in the main input member of the reduction gear which, in vibration terms, effectively de-coupled the propeller from the crankshaft. The coupling comprised spring sections at the periphery running in slots between driver and driven segments shaped to give variable rate. The only previous airborne example of this coupling had been in the Beardmore diesel engine application for the R101 airship and in their application to the Maybach engines of the Graf Zeppelin.

Development led to the engines being uprated to 400hp and the incorporation of a thrust augmenter system inducing cooling air with the ejected exhaust and the benefit of lower airframe drag.

The Queen 30 engine had a related career starting with a military contract for the Percival Prentice trainer and subsequently being applied to the four-engined Heron airliner which flew in 1950. The engine incorporated similar cylinders to the Queen 70, but was otherwise reminiscent of the earlier Queens. Comparison with the Queen 70, of similar capacity but with 8½lb supercharge and geared propeller allowing higher running speed, is instructive in that 400hp at 3,000rpm at take-off conditions compares with 240hp at 2,500rpm for the simpler engine.

Major 215 helicopter engine

In 1956 the company ran a completely re-designed Major engine described initially as the 'Utility Major,' which found its application in the Saunders Roe Skeeter helicopter airframe. This engine had the same bore and stroke as the later Queens and utilised fuel injection with a compression ratio of 7.25 to give 215hp at a one-hour rating.

In 1958 a turbo-blown version of the engine was developed which raised the power marginally within the limits of the airframe transmission but allowed this power to be developed at the higher altitude required by military helicopter operation in the Far East. The turbocharger was of interest in utilising the supercharger impeller components of the Queen 70 driven by a small turbine machined from the solid by an early application of electro-chemical machining and driven from the engine exhaust pipes with a nozzle-less scroll. Flight trials were undertaken in the Skeeter but the unit did not enter service.

Motor Cycles again, and the Water Gipsy

This account of the de Havilland piston engines started with motor cycles and concludes in a similar vein. In 1952 the company had a short period of peripheral involvement with the motor cycle engine. Vincent H R D, at their factory in Stevenage, were developing a flight edition of the 'Black Shadow' motor cycle engine, the 'Picador'. This was being undertaken under a Ministry contract for a

Major 215 on Stag Lane test bed in 1958 with turbo supercharger.

Sir Geoffrey de Havilland, F B Halford and John Brodie in a light-hearted pose revering the Gipsy in a Chipmunk.

propeller-driven target drone with airframe activity undertaken by M L Aviation. The engine had been developed for airborne application at a short life rating at 70hp for the 1,000cc unit with testing undertaken on a dynamometer bench.

When the requirement arose to prove the engine with a propeller the Ministry approached de Havillands to provide the necessary facilities. A test bed at Hatfield, originally built for Rolls-Royce Merlin work and subsequently adapted for Gipsy propeller testing, was allocated and modified for this work. Test site personnel viewed the work with some enthusiasm and the development programme was rapidly completed. The combination of the high-revving air-cooled engine with its propeller and twin megaphone exhausts produced a most remarkable sound, much loved by the motor cycle fraternity, and the selection of the remote site at Hatfield was obviously a wise choice.

The swan-song of piston engine activity occurred in the early 1960s with developments somewhat uncharacteristic of the maturing industry but reflecting the general spirit of that decade. Industrial diversity was being practiced, applying the aircraft engine industries acumen to the market place. As a consequence of the 1957 Government White Paper, which presupposed all military aviation business being phased out and replaced by guided missiles, a number of industrial activities were investigated including manufacturing turbo-blowers for British Railway's new locomotives, development of early examples of garage forecourt dispensing equipment, which subsequently revolutionised that particular market, and development of small two-stroke engines.

Dr. Joe Ehrlich brought to the company a life-time's experience of motor cycle two-stroke engines and the particular concept of the 'boost-port'. In simplified terms this supplemented the normal transfer and exhaust passages, working in conjunction with the piston, by providing chambers communicating with the cylinder at approximately the mid-stroke position. On the induction stroke they received part of the charge then subsequently trapped by the piston and released into the cylinder/combustion chamber at the power stroke thus sustaining pressure, enhancing the brake mean effective pressure and energising the exhaust flow.

Impressive development work was undertaken which led to a programme for development of an outboard engine matched to the then-expanding boating leisure market. The Water Gipsy was a 150cc unit giving 10hp, and development went through the phases of bench testing of the basic engine on the dynamometer and then of the complete outboard motor unit, with water tank testing and practically with boats. Units of similar size were installed experimentally in motor cycle frames – with impressive and somewhat startling results – and also in rotavators.

Although the primary purpose of these boost-port units was high torque availability and general slogging performance, a parallel related line of development was the development of third-port racing engines matched to the 125cc motorcycle formula. With these developments, the works rider Rex Avery, after a number of successes, eventually found himself sharing machines with Mike Hailwood. In 1961 the DH/EMC machine was highly competitive, with 27hp at 10,000rpm, and at the Good Friday meeting at Brands Hatch it was first in a five-lap race and a quarter of a mile in front of the opposition. At the Thruxton meeting, it broke Hailwood's Ducati lap record by 5mph. In 1962, at the Silverstone meeting, the DH/EMC came first, second and third in the 125 event ridden by Hailwood, Minter and Avery. In the T.T. in that year, the main contenders for the 125 event were Honda and Suzuki. Hailwood, Driver and Avery were competing with the DH/EMC machines and

'Water Gipsies' on test.

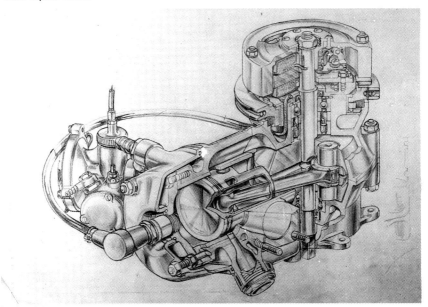

Sectional drawing of DH/Ehrlich 'Water Gipsy' 10hp outboard.

through the event Hailwood was pressing the leader on the Honda who, with this incentive, achieved the first 90mph lap by a 125 machine. Unfortunately, on the final lap the EMC stopped, with the result that Honda took the first five places and Rex Avery on the EMC finished sixth.

These events coincided with the final phase of existence of the de Havilland Engine Co. as an individual public company in the aircraft industry, and with the emergent new company relationships work on the projected DH/EMC activities was phased out.

Montage of newspaper headlines and photograph, 125cc DH/E M C with Mike Hailwood.

D.H. piston engine manufacture to circa 1960.

Iris	6-10 approx.
Gipsy I	1445
”　II	309
”　III	611
Minor	171
Major 1	14,615
”　2	91
”　8	952
”　10	1,248
Major 200/215	106
Gipsy Six I	1,139
”　”　II	248
Gipsy King	90 approx.
Queen 2	1,681
Queen 3	1,358
Queen 30	1,762
Queen 70	1,889
Water Gipsy	12 approx.

Chapter 5
THE JET PROPULSION ERA

Jet Propulsion

Through the 1930s, and as a by-product of the advancing technology of aviation and the supercharged piston engine, emerged the practical realisation of long-held engineers' dreams for the application of gas turbine and rocket engines to the jet propulsion of aircraft. In 1929 Fritz von Opel in Germany achieved take-off and a short flight with a rocket-powered aircraft. In 1930 Whittle registered his primary patent combining the gas turbine with jet propulsion and brought this to practical realisation with the bench running of a prototype engine on 12 April 1937.

The first flight powered by a gas turbine was achieved in Germany on 27 August 1939, with flight of the Heinkel He178 powered by a HeS3b engine developed under that company's support and patronage from a prototype unit, by a young engineer Dr. Pabst von Ohain, which ran initially a few months after Whittle's engine in September 1937. The Heinkel company also, in 1939, undertook the first flight of a liquid-propellant rocket engine in a fighter aircraft, the He112, initially as a booster unit and subsequently as primary powerplant for take-off and flight. In Italy the Caproni company collaborated with the inventor Campini in developing and flying, in August 1940, the CC1 aircraft which utilised a ducted piston engine driving a three-stage axial compressor with afterburning to provide jet propulsion.

Frank Whittle was a serving RAF officer and for five years after registration of his patent took no active steps to implement his ideas. In 1936 however, capital was raised and a company, Power Jets Limited, was established. Prototype manufacture was contracted to British Thomson Houston Ltd. (BTH), the established and respected company whose products included steam turbines. Following the run of the 'U' engine in 1937, development concentrated on the requirements for flight, primarily in achieving a compact combustion system to replace the extended duct arrangement that gave the first prototype its name.

In March 1938 the potential of the invention was recognised officially and an Air Ministry contract awarded for a flight engine designated W1. The project was still considered of relatively low priority and a contract for the construction of a suitable airframe, to Air Ministry Specification E28/39, was not placed until August 1939, at which time the German Heinkel aeroplane flew on the eve of war.

In 1940 the Ministry of Aircraft Production decided that if quantity production of the new invention was to be achieved, the design expertise of Power Jets needed to be supplemented by association with a company experienced in manufacture. Discussions were held with the management of car manufacturers, including Rover and Vauxhall, and a production contract was awarded to the Rover Motor Company for manufacture of the Power Jets unit, in addition to the work they were undertaking on manufacture and repair of Bristol aero engines.

On 15 May 1941, the Gloster-Whittle E28/39 aircraft W4041 flew with the Whittle W1 engine, the first jet-propelled aircraft of the allied powers.

The Goblin

In January 1941 the de Havilland Aircraft Company were knowledgeable of the jet propulsion developments and, whilst being fully committed to the Mosquito, were conscious of the limitations which were imposed by propeller propulsion at flight speed above 400mph. Having designed a bomber which could outpace virtually all contemporary fighters they were particularly interested in the ability presented to remove this barrier.

Major Halford had since 1937 occupied a suite of offices provided by de Havilland at the Stag Lane works and at this time he and his team were responsible for developments in the designs of the Sabre piston engine for Napier in addition to the DH Gipsy engines and DH propellers. Vauxhall sought advice on the aeronautical aspects of the work which the Air Ministry considered placing on them. Consequent on this, talks were held between Major Halford and Sir Henry Tizzard at the Air Ministry and as a result, in April 1941, DH was awarded a contract for the design and development of a jet propulsion engine to be matched to the Company's concept of a single-seat high performance fighter.

A thrust requirement of 3,000lb was determined, thus giving the equivalent of 3,000hp in terms of current propeller efficiency at the then operational heights and with the potential for speed in excess of 500mph and much higher ceiling. Diameter was to be limited to 50in to give a minimal fuselage diameter matched to the seated pilot.

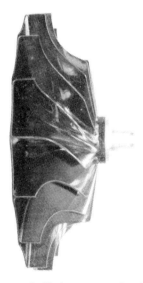

The Sabre piston engines single-sided supercharger impeller compared with the compressor impeller configuration of the 'Goblin' engine.

Whilst capitalising to the full on the work of Whittle and Power Jets, Halford followed an independent line with the aim of maximum installed efficiency. The Whittle engines utilised a double-sided impeller for the compressor and reverse-flow combustion chambers with the intent of producing a compact unit with a short rotative assembly. Halford had recently modified the supercharger arrangement in the Sabre by substituting a single-sided impeller with integral curved inlet guide vanes for the former double-sided unit, and had established higher overall efficiency. The engine now evolved used a direct-scaled version of the Sabre impeller, and probably as a consequence of this prime feature it was designated through its prototype phase as the 'H.1 Supercharger'. Straight-through combustion chambers were developed and the turbine and compressor were connected by a large diameter rigid shaft. These provisions gave a simple and compact layout assuring reliability, with both internal gas flow paths and external profile well-matched to the aerodynamic requirements of both the engine and its airframe installations.

Design commenced in April, 1941, initial drawings were issued on 8 August 1941 to a newly segregated section of the de Havilland engine manufacturing organisation operating through the war years at the former Garage premises of Messrs Car Mart Ltd at the Welsh Harp Lake area to the South of the Stag Lane, Edgware, works. The prototype engine commenced bench running at Hatfield on 13 April 1942. The following day an Air Ministry contract was placed for the manufacture of three prototype DH100 aircraft, the preliminary design of which had been matched and integrated with that of the engine.

By September, 200 hours of bench testing had been completed with two engines, this work being supplemented by combustion chamber testing utilising, as an air supply, the compressed air arrangements established at the partially-completed Dartford tunnel to keep the river waters out of the workings. Later, a power station steam turbine set at Northampton was utilised for engine compressor aerodynamic development with the provision of a step-up gearbox. This provided 5,000hp, allowing part-load testing against the requirement of the compressor for 6,000hp at 10,000rpm. On 26 September 1942 the engine, subsequently named 'Goblin', completed a 25 hour flight approval test and thus was available for flight development work and awaited the availability of an aeroplane.

At this time the Gloster Meteor prototype aircraft, which had been built against Air Ministry specification F9/40 for an operational jet fighter utilising the Power Jets/Rover W2B, awaited engines powerful enough for flight. Taxi tests had been undertaken on prototype DG205 on 10 July with engines at 1,000lb thrust but development problems did not allow attainment of the intended 1,800lb rating. The Goblin, designed as a 3,000lb engine, was inherently larger and could meet the flight case. The Air Ministry therefore arranged for the second prototype under construction to be modified to accept this engine. This aircraft, DG206, flew on the 5 March 1943, with its Goblin engines derated to give 1,500lb thrust at 8,000rpm.

Early development flying was thus undertaken with the Goblin, joined by the W2B-powered prototype DG205 from 12 June 1943. Later development of this aircraft, the first British operational jet fighter, proceeded with the Rolls-Royce development of the W2B, the Welland, taken over from Rover and subsequently the Derwent I and Derwent V, engines of similar configuration to the Goblin but retaining the double-sided impeller.

On 20 September 1943, the first prototype of the DH100 flew with its Goblin engine. The aircraft was initially dubbed 'Spider Crab' but subsequently became the

The "H1 Supercharger" engine as initially designated and tested on a Hatfield open test bed from April 1942.

Gloster-de Havilland group after the first flight of the H1 powered Gloster F9/40 on 5 March 1943. Mr. G Bristow is second from the left, on his left is Mr M Daunt, Gloster Chief Test Pilot. On Mr Daunt's left is Mr J L P Brodie, director-in-charge of the de Havilland Engineering Division.
On 28 February Michael Daunt inspecting the aircraft on pre flight checks was suddenly sucked into the port engine intake, so far that his tie end was cut off by the compressor. Guy Bristow's quick response in shutting down the engine avoided more serious injury.

49

The Goblin powered prototypes of the Meteor, Vampire and the American P80 Shooting Star.

Vampire. Its configuration, with a minimal fuselage housing cockpit, equipment and engine, allowed direct intake airflow from wing root intakes and direct discharge of the propulsive flow from the engine exhaust. The tail assembly was carried clear of the jet efflux by the twin-boom arrangement. In January, 1944, the American Lockheed P80 Shooting Star flew for the first time also with a Goblin and in the spring of that year these two aircraft became the first in their respective countries to exceed 500mph. In January 1945 the Goblin engine became the first British military turbojet to receive an official 150hr type test certificate.

Production of the Vampire was initially undertaken by the English Electric Co. since the de Havilland shops were fully committed to Mosquito production, and the type did not enter service with the RAF until the end of the war in 1945. On 3 December 1945, the Vampire became the first jet-propelled aeroplane to take off and land on an aircraft carrier. The Vampire, with its Goblin engine, continued in production well into the 1950s. A two-seat night fighter version was produced for the RAF in 1949 and a trainer in 1950. The Vampire fighter became the first jet-propelled fighter for 12 overseas air forces, the trainer version entered service with some 20 foreign air forces, and a total of over 5,000 Goblin engines were built in the United Kingdom and under licence abroad.

Goblin 2 engine alongside Vampire at Royal Air Force Museum.

The Vampire, a major export success of the post war era introducing jet propulsion to some 20 overseas air forces.

Ceremonial shut down of Goblin on test at Hatfield, 31 March 1949, following demonstration of reliability and engine endurance at 1000hrs. Air Marshall Sir Alec Coryton then Controller of Supplies (Air) closes throttle and shut off cock.

Vampire with Goblin re-heat experiment c 1949.

Recognising the commercial potential of these new developments, Major Halford joined the de Havilland Aircraft Co. in 1943 to concentrate on gas turbine work and in February 1944 the de Havilland Engine Company was constituted as a separate but subsidiary company. At the end of 1944 Stonegrove, a recently completed factory in the green belt area to the immediate north of Edgware, was tooled-up specifically for the production of Goblin engines.

At the end of the war DH immediately made plans to re-enter the civil market and logically proposed to capitalise on its jet aircraft experience. In the final war years the Brabazon Committee had been set up to specify a number of aircraft type specifications to ensure development of a civil aviation industry. One of these was for a fast and high altitude mail and passenger-carrying jet-propelled airliner. The specification evolved to satisfaction in the DH106 Comet, but an initial proposal was for a swept-wing tailless aircraft to be powered by three Goblin engines in its rear fuselage.

Goblins and Ghosts awaiting final clearance in the major production days of the 1950s.

53

The Goblin powered DH108 following its first flight, 15 May 1946 with the near traditional gathering of notabilities including its pilot Geoffrey de Havilland junior, Sir Geoffrey de Havilland and F B Halford.

DH108 on its 1948 closed circuit record flight of 605.23mph.

Ghost rotative assembly. Compressor, impeller and turbine.

DH Comet 1 prototype in early flight trials in 1949 over Hertfordshire.

de Havilland Engine Company team responsible for the development of the Ghost engine for the Comet 1.

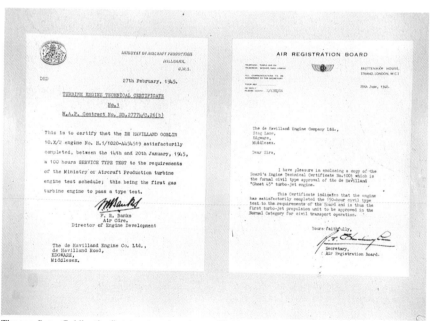

The two firsts. Goblin, the first type tested engine certified by Ministry of Aircraft Production, Ghost first civil engines certified by the Air Registration Board.

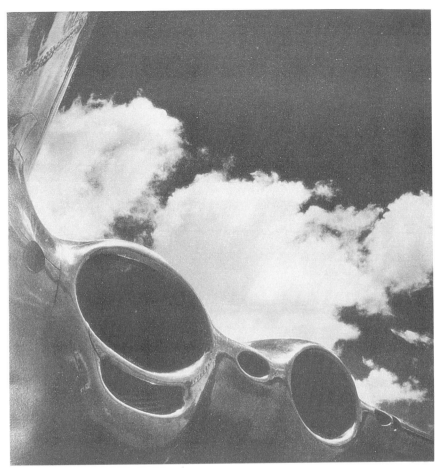

'Jet Portrait' a classic photograph by Henry Hensser.

The single-seat DH108 aircraft was built utilising a Vampire fuselage with the addition of a sharply swept wing and a vertical tail fin only. It flew on 16 May 1946, and two further prototypes, one specifically for low speed trials, were built. Trials showed that the tailless configuration would result in a landing speed too fast for a practical airliner, but experience continued to be gained for fighter development.

A number of records were broken by these aircraft and on 6 September 1948 the DH108, with its Goblin engine uprated to 3,700lb thrust, became the first British aircraft to exceed the speed of sound. Sadly all three aircraft were lost in fatal crashes including, on 27 September 1946, the death of Geoffrey de Havilland, eldest son of the founder of the company, when the aircraft broke up over the Thames estuary on the eve of an attempt on the world speed record.

'Morning Glory' - The new travellers world of the Comet highway - Henry Hensser.

Sir Malcolm Campbell and Peter du Cane, in company with F B Halford, examining the Goblin on test in 1947 for the subsequently abortive trials on the jet propulsion of the pre-war water speed record holder 'Bluebird'.

The Ghost

In 1943 the design of a large engine for fighter applications was put in hand. This engine, the Ghost, was of similar configuration to the Goblin but with a 36in diameter impeller replacing that of 31in, and mass flow increased from 60 to 88lb/sec. The engine was to be twice as powerful as the then contemporary engines and it ran in October 1945, soon demonstrating thrusts at 4,400lb. In May 1947 flight development commenced in a modified Vampire, followed in August in a Lancastrian airliner, development of the Lancaster bomber, with two Ghosts replacing the outboard Merlin engines. In March 1948 the engine, fitted in a Vampire airframe and flown by John Cunningham, established a world altitude record at 59,492ft.

The first application of the engine was in the Swedish SAAB J29 aircraft in 1948. This 650mph single-engined fighter, designed specifically around the Ghost engine, followed an earlier twin-boomed piston engine type, the J21, which had been converted and powered by a Goblin engine; these developments reflecting the strong position that the early DH jet engines enjoyed in the European market.

In June 1948 the Ghost Mk.50 became the first gas turbine to obtain the status of full approval for civil operation with fare-paying passengers under Air Registration Board regulations, thus complementing the similar distinction earned by the Goblin in the military field three years earlier.

On 27 July 1949, the de Havilland Comet airliner flew from Hatfield and after an intensive development period and route proving trials entered service with BOAC on 2 May 1952, initially on the London-Johannesburg route, as the world's first civil jet airliner. For this application the engine was developed to 5,300lb thrust, allowing a full 5,000lb applied thrust with the long tailpipes featured in the clean wing-root installation of the Comet, perpetuated in the Nimrod but since abandoned in civil airliners.

John Cobb's 'Crusader' with its Ghost engine awaiting launch on Coniston in 1952.

The engine in this application was a maid-of-all-work in driving all the aircraft's power accessories, providing compressor bleed air for passenger cabin pressurisation and airframe de-icing. For the Comet 1a aeroplane, which was designed for operation from hot and high airfields, a Mk2 variant of the engine was produced with water/methanol injection into the combustion chambers. This restored take-off thrust to that available in temperate areas and thus maintain full passenger carrying capability.

In 1954 operation of the Comet 1 aircraft on passenger-carrying services was terminated following the two disasters in the Mediterranean off the coast of Italy. The aircraft broke up and crashed into the sea, with the loss of all on board, as a result of fatigue failure of the pressurised fuselage. Substantial wreckage of the aircraft G-ALYP, which had crashed off Elba on 10 January 1954, was recovered from the sea bed. This included the aircraft's centre section which retained the four engines substantially intact with the exception that the turbine disc from the No. 2 engine was missing.

Whilst suspicion was initially focused on this as a possible cause of the accident, it was established that the turbine shroud showed no evidence of passage of either blade or disc indicating that the turbine had been shed as the aircraft broke up. When stripped, the nominally complete engines all showed signs of cracking and incipient failure at the turbine hubs. It was established that this was the result of the generation of a destructive gyroscopic couple as an interaction of a rapid rotation of the whole wing about a transverse axis whilst the engines were still running normally.

The official accident enquiry states "such a rotation, being about an axis at right angles to the engine shafts would produce gyroscopic couples tending to bend the shafts in a sideways direction, that is, in the plane of the wing. Since the clearance between the discs and the stationary parts surrounding them are small, signs of rubbing would be expected in definite regions. Examination showed such signs in each engine". Tests at Hatfield, using a rig in which a single engine was run and swung through an arc under the influence of its weight and thrust, reproduced the failure at conditions corresponding to engines and wing section turning upside down in about one second.

At the time of the disasters the Ghost had attained 1,000 hours between overhauls

60

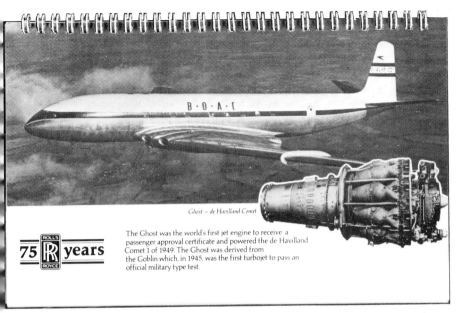

Ghost – de Havilland Comet

The Ghost was the world's first jet engine to receive a passenger approval certificate and powered the de Havilland Comet 1 of 1949. The Ghost was derived from the Goblin which, in 1945, was the first turbojet to pass an official military type test.

75 R years

Triumph & Tragedy. On 2 may 1952 the Comet 1 entered service with B O A C as the world's first jet propelled airliner. In 1954 structural failure grounded the aircraft as a consequence of fatigue of the pressurised fuselage. The 'Ghost' engines were absolved.

with a low incidence of in-flight shutdowns. From 1952 however the Comet II had been under development at increased weight and power with axial-flow Rolls-Royce Avon engines for RAF duties and when, in 1958, the Comet IV re-entered civil service it was as a considerably modified and larger aeroplane with Avon engines at 10,500lb thrust.

In September 1949 the Ghost engine powered the prototype of the new DH Venom fighter which was a logical development of the Vampire fitted with a wing with a swept leading edge to give transonic performance. The Venom soon entered service with the RAF and was followed by the Mk.3 two-seat night fighter in 1953 and the Sea Venom in 1956. Its fuel system was innovative. Some marks continued the use of the then almost universal Lucas fuel system with simple vortex burners, but others utilised the Dowty spill flow system which at that time gave improved altitude performance due to the wider operating envelope of the burners.

The Venom aircraft served into the '60s, making a very strong operational contribution. Its early success as a day fighter and ground attack aircraft related to the fact that it was the earliest of the 'swept' wing fighters to be operational. The truly swept-wing Hunter fighter had a longer gestation period from its earlier straight-wing predecessors, and the Swift aircraft, developed from the straight-wing naval Attacker, ran into operational problems which finally led to its cancellation. The Venom also continued long in service as the prime operational night fighter due to delays and limitation in the ability of the intended replacement, the Gloster Javelin, to meet requirements.

Comet disaster investigation, Ghost on swing rig for turbine disk destructive gyroscopic couple investigation.

Nearly 2,000 Ghosts were built and they were licence-produced in Sweden, Switzerland and Italy.

In 1952 John Cobb built the jet-propelled motor boat 'Crusader', powered by a Ghost engine, for an attempt of the world water speed record. This followed abortive attempts by Sir Malcolm Campbell in 1947-48 to improve on the performance of his pre-war boat 'Bluebird K3' with the installation of a Goblin. John Cobb was killed when 'Crusader' broke up at 240mph on 29 September 1952, when making a record attempt on Loch Ness.

H.3 and Comet Cabin Blower

In 1945, with the company active in the jet propulsion field, Major Halford and his team prepared a design for a gas turbine Gipsy replacement, and a 500hp turboprop engine was built and run in 1946-47. The engine featured a two-stage centrifugal compressor directly coupled to a three-stage turbine and through a reduction gear to its propeller. Individual reverse-flow combustion chambers were utilised. The engine was intended to power a pressurised development of the DH Dove. The engine was only run on the test bed at limited power and development terminated when the government withdrew support from all small turbine development. Competitive engines had also been projected; the Janus by Bristol and the Nymph by Napier. This latter name suggested, along with the Naiad, an intriguing 'spirit' association with the engine naming policy for the Halford/DH engine series.

Also in the 1947-48 period a three-stage centrifugal cabin supercharger intended for the Comet airliner was built and test run extensively. This unit was intended to be

62

installed in the wing leading edge between the two engine intakes with drive shafts from the engine pair, clutching and speed control being arranged with scoop-controlled fluid couplings. In the event, the facts that the Ghost featured positive metered lubrication to its front bearing at only ½ pint per hour, and complete purity of engine compressor discharge air was demonstrated on test, allowed the deletion of this ancillary from the aircraft.

The Gyron

In the late 1940s the application of axial compressors to jet propulsion engines was well-established and both Rolls-Royce, typically with the Avon, and Armstrong Siddeley with the Sapphire had engines of this type in production. de Havillands persisted with the centrifugal compressor, running test rigs in attempting to retain the simplicity of the centrifugal rotating impeller to impose velocity, and part compression, whilst modifying the principle by turning the air flow at high speed and diffusing it axially to complete the pressure cycle. Losses proved to be high, however, and the state of the art at that time limited compression ratios to the order of 4 to 1. In comparison, contemporary axial compressors, which impose velocity with rotating axial blades and convert this to pressure with a complementing stationary axial blade, could achieve a ratio of approximately 1.25 per stage. Thus it required, say, six stages for a similar performance and the ability, with increasing complexity, to multiply blade stages to give high cycle/engine efficiencies.

The de Havilland Engine Co started work on the Gyron axial flow engine as the H.4 in 1950. The name Gyron perpetuated an earlier use by Whittle of the word Gyrone. He evolved it to convey something that goes 'round and round' in contrast with the established aircraft engine understood as going 'up and down'. His intent had been to market the Power Jets products under this generic name. With participation of the established manufacturers swamping what was visualised as Power Jets market, the name did not gain favour although when the E28/39 pioneer aeroplane first flew, initial publicity again used the title Gyrone for that aircraft. Its use by de Havilland without the 'e' when the engine was first publicised in the mid-1950s is best explained as a compliment by Major Halford and the Company to Sir Frank Whittle.

The Gyron concept was for a doubling of power over contemporary engines, with minimal practical weight and frontal area, and matched to the requirement for supersonic flight in military application. A moderate compression ratio at 6 to 1 was aimed at, initially with a six-stage axial compressor and subsequently with seven stages, on the basis of supersonic reheated operation at Mach 2 achieving an overall compression ratio of the order of 40 to 1 with intake compression in the airframe. The limited engine compression element related to the twin criteria of simplicity of the engine, and limiting of the overall temperature rise in the intake/compressor/combustion system to a figure allowing uncooled rotor blades in Nimonic 100/90 material.

The engine designated the D.Gy.1 ran on 5 January 1953 at Hatfield and soon achieved its design thrust at 15,000lb dry and 20,000lb with afterburning. At that time and for most of the decade it was the most powerful engine in the world. The basic engine was 13ft long with a diameter of 4ft 6in at the relatively low weight of 4,270lb; compression ratio was at 6 to 1 utilising a seven-stage compressor and a two-stage turbine with this assembly perpetuating the de Havilland practice of a simple two-bearing system with a large tapered drum attachment between compress-

Model of the H3 500hp turboprop of 1947.

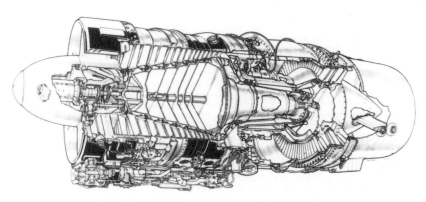

DE HAVILLAND GYRON SENIOR TURBOJET

The Gyron Senior Turbo-jet. Under development from 1953 initially as a private venture and at that time the world's most powerful engine.

Short Sperrin in flight in 1955 with Gyron Senior in lower port position.

Test bed underside view, Gyron Senior on reheat.

The Hawker P1121 mock up with its Gyron Senior engine in the foreground. Type tested in 1955 at 20,000lb thrust and 25,000lb with reheat for this application.

or and turbine. Specific fuel consumption was at .95lb/lb/hr for the basic engine which compared well with contemporary engines and suggested potential application in other than the military supersonic case.

The first flight-standard engine, designated D.Gy.2, ran in September 1954, at a static thrust uprated to 20,000lb dry. The engine flew in a converted Short Sperrin bomber on 7 July 1955, initially replacing the lower port Avon engine of this rather unconventional four-engined straight-wing aeroplane and the following year with Gyrons in both port and starboard lower nacelles. Tests proceeded unreheated to altitudes of 50,000ft plus. In 1955 the engine passed its Government type test at 20,000lb dry and 25,000lb reheated and awaited its first application. Installation was intended in the Avro 730 supersonic bomber and the single-engined Hawker P1121 Interceptor, both of which were under construction with Government contracts.

In April 1957 the Government White Paper was published, cancelling virtually all advanced manned military aircraft then under construction in favour of concentration on missiles for defence. Work stopped immediately on the Avro 730 bomber but since Hawker had extreme confidence in the potential of the P1121, construction of the prototype continued under private venture funding into 1958 when it was finally abandoned. The Gyron also continued as a private venture through this phase, and at the cessation of work in August 1958, thrust levels at 29,300lb were demonstrated.

Buccaneer on flight shed apron at Hatfield with Gyron Junior.

As an interesting aside, in subsequent years the 'all missile' decision of 1957 was seen to be a mistake and the world's military powers continued the deployment of manned aircraft. The contemporary Russian aircraft, the Mig 25 'Foxbat', which is still seen as a considerable threat to the defences of the West, is powered by a Tumansky R266 engine. This engine, which dates from the early '60s, follows the same concepts and construction features as the Gyron. 'Janes All the World's Aircraft' for 1980-81 described it as having a five-stage compressor at the modest compression ratio of 7 to 1, a single-stage uncooled turbine, and developing thrusts at 20,500lb dry and 27,010lb with reheat.

The Gyron Junior

With the performance of the Gyron and its efficient axial compressor proven, the decision was made to capitalise on the work undertaken to produce a three-fifths scale engine to compete in the wider market of medium thrust engines by virtue of its competitive fuel consumption, low weight and frontal area, and simplicity of design promising high serviceability. In August 1955 the engine first ran, delivering its rating of 7,000lb thrust, and it flew in a Canberra flying test bed in August 1957. A particular feature of the engine was that its compressor allowed easy handling, aided by variable inlet guide vanes only, and did not have the dependency demanded by most contemporary engines of requiring external air bleed to allow acceleration.

The engine was selected for the Blackburn NA39 naval strike aircraft which it powered on its first flight in April 1958. This aircraft was developed as the Buccaneer, with its distinctive area-rule bottle-shaped fuselage and requirement to operate fast and low for long periods. A unique feature was its dependence on a comprehensive boundary layer control system and blown flaps to provide low speed approach and deck touchdown ability in contrast to its high speed capability. Placing dependence on wide compressor operating characteristics the engine was required to provide a compressed air bleed at approximately 17.5% of its full throttle mass flow

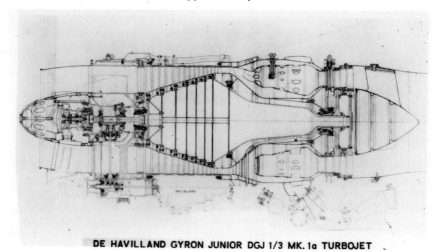

DE HAVILLAND GYRON JUNIOR DGJ 1/3 MK. 1a TURBOJET

Long section drawing of Gyron Junior.

Gyron Juniors in production at Leavesden.

for these aircraft services. The Buccaneer Mk.1 undertook its deck landing trials on HMS Victorious in January 1960 and, following type approval of the engine as the DGJ Mk. 101, the aircraft entered service with the Royal Navy. It was phased out in the early '70s, as the Mk.2 aeroplane entered service powered by Rolls-Royce Spey engines, in fulfilment of classic aircraft development demands for more thrust as weight and drag on operational aircraft are increased, and with the benefit of reduced fuel consumption from the bypass engine improving range.

The PS50 Gyron Junior

On 4 October 1957 this scale edition of the Gyron ran, extending to the smaller scale the supersonic capability of the original design. Designated initially as the DGJ10 the engine was rated at 10,000lb thrust dry and its operational capability matched it to a 2,000°K afterburner and variable exhaust nozzle to give 14,000lb sea level thrust and 20,000lb when at Mach 2 at 36,000ft.

In January 1961 flight trials commenced in a modified Gloster Javelin aircraft. Extensive tests were also undertaken in the National Gas Turbine Establishment's high altitude test plant at Farnborough to its full Mach 2.5 range. These tests were the first to exercise the full capability of this major national investment for supersonic aircraft development. The engine pioneered a number of features with its stainless steel and titanium construction and its high temperature requirements on its oil and fuel systems. It was the first British engine capable of sustained running at the high inlet pressure and temperature conditions imposed by continuous supersonic operations.

The Gyron Junior PS50, the second de Havilland engine for supersonic flight, first ran on 12 August 1955. This photograph, taken in the Gyron Junior testbed after the event, shows, from left to right: Mr G Bristow, Chief Test Engineer, Dr E S Moult, Director and Chief Engineer, Mr F M Owner, Deputy Chief Engineer, Mr S W G Beard, Design Engineer, Gyron Junior, Dr P H Calder, Engineer in Charge, Gas Dynamics Laboratory, Dr D M Cockburn, Performance Engineer and Mr W T Winter, Chief Development Engineer.

The intended and initially-contracted application for the engine was to be the mixed-power Saunders Roe 177 high altitude interceptor with its gas turbine complemented by a DH Spectre rocket engine. This combination of rocket and turbine power gave high speed and acceleration at ultra-high altitudes, whilst still allowing considerable range and endurance at medium altitudes. Work had been initiated by the flights of the SR53 from May 1957 with its Spectre engine complemented by a small Armstrong Siddeley Viper turbojet to give cruise capabilities. In the event the SR177 did not fly. In the post-1957 White Paper period the contract was initially maintained since the aircraft was considered as a near-missile, and additionally the German services were actively interested, but by 1959 the project was cancelled.

Development of the engine continued on a research basis, however, as was that of a further application, the Bristol 188 high speed research aeroplane. This had initially been projected as a twin-engined aerodynamic scale research aeroplane with the aerodynamic features of the Avro 730 supersonic bomber. With the demise of this project the programme for the 188 was, rather exceptionally, continued to further development of stainless steel aircraft structure and the supersonic engine application with respect to the Concorde programme.

The Bristol 188 flew on 14 April 1962 powered by two Gyron Junior DGJ10 engines. Flight trials took the aeroplane to a speed of Mach 1.88 and, whilst a lot of valuable information was gained, development was overtaken by the availability and outstanding performance of the Concorde development prototypes.

Artist's impression of the Bristol 188 in flight.

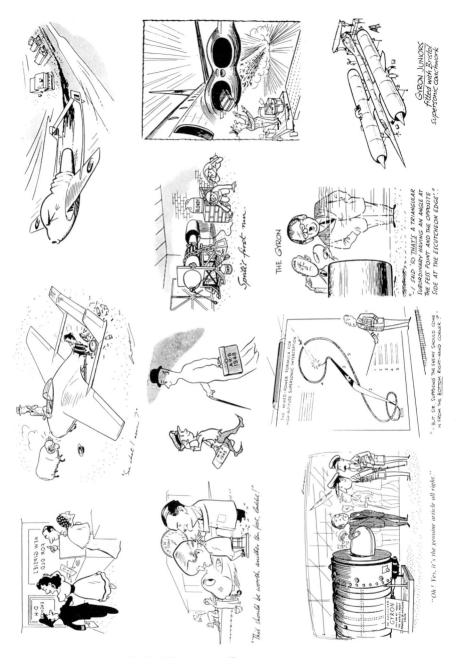

Wren cartoons from the de Havilland Gazette personify an era.

Chapter 6
ROCKET ENGINES FOR AIRCRAFT PROPULSION

Rocket engines, providing propulsion by direct reaction to a controlled 'explosion' of a fuel and an oxidant, originated in early history and the first illustration of a rocket-propelled aeroplane dates from 1420 in the form of a model bird derivation of a stick-stabilised rocket. The first liquid propellant rockets evolved from parallel pioneer endeavours in Germany and the USA during the 1920s and opened the way for sustained power.

Major effort was applied in Germany in the 1930s in support of re-armament. von Opel's flight with solid propellant rockets in 1929 marked the enthusiastic approach and the flight of the He112 with its Walter engine in 1939 demonstrated both the first assisted take-off and subsequent main propulsion application of liquid rockets to aircraft flight. The first flight of the A4/V2 von Braun-Dornberger rocket missile in 1942 initiated the era of space flight.

German efforts in the war years laid the foundation for all subsequent rocket activity. Solid 'slowed' explosives were quickly superseded by liquid propellants for aircraft and missile application, and by the end of the war years particular fields of application had evolved for the liquid oxidants available. Liquid oxygen was primarily applied to large missiles, and vied with red fuming nitric acid in the field of medium-to-small missiles. High strength hydrogen peroxide, described as high test peroxide or HTP, evolved as the propellant for aircraft applications. The oxidants were used either by themselves as mono-propellants or supplemented in the engine's combustion chambers by hydrocarbon fuels as bi-propellants.

British aircraft propulsion work through the war years was limited to the application of solid cordite-type propellants for assisted take-off, primarily for Fleet Air Arm operations. Units were evolved by the Rocket Propulsion Section of the RAE, standardised virtually on what was described as the 5in Assisted Take-Off Unit. A unit weighing 66lb gave a thrust of 1,200lb for 4 seconds and, typically, 4 of these units would be utilised by a Seafire aircraft in adverse take-off conditions.

Virtually all of the German aircraft propulsion rocket engine work was undertaken by the Walterwerke. The Walter 109/500 was the primary ATO unit initially as a mono-propellant type but subsequently bi-propellant. Typical performance was a thrust of 1,200lb sustained for 29 seconds in contrast with British and American practice. The Messerschmitt Me163, the first operational rocket-propelled fighter, was powered by a Walter 109/509 bi-propellant engine which provided a thrust of 4,400lb for the 4 minutes powered endurance provided by the aircraft's tankage.

Sprite & Super Sprite

In 1946 a rocket propulsion section was formed with a team of four under the leadership of A V Cleaver, who had previously been a propeller specialist and was a long term enthusiast for rockets and space flight as a member of the British Interplanetary Society. Initial investigations were aided by the considerable repository of German archive and design material, together with items of equipment, obtained by way of post-war reparations and lodged with the Government Rocket Establishment at Westcott, Bucks, and RAE Farnborough.

In 1947, with flight development of the Ghost engine proceeding in the Lancastrian flying test bed, an opportunity was taken by the rocket team to gain practical experience by the fitment of Walter 109/500 ATO units to this aircraft and flight trials were undertaken in '47-48 to a total of 8 take-offs.

Design work commenced on an assisted take-off engine, the Sprite, rated at 5,000lb thrust for 16 seconds with a dry weight of 350lb and fuelled weight of 925lb. High test peroxide was contained in a pressurised stainless steel tank and this was fed to the propulsion chamber encircled by an additional pressurised tank containing calcium permanganate. This was also injected into the chamber as a catalyst, decomposing the peroxide to form a propulsion jet of steam at 600°C. The engine ran on a test bed at Hatfield in November 1949.

The design intent was to provide take-off boost for tropical operations of the Comet aircraft and the design of this incorporated units between the twin jet pipes in the wing trailing edge. In May 1951 flight trials commenced with the Comet prototype, G-ALVG, following 18 months of engine development with some 220 trial firings.

In the event, the performance of the Comet and its Ghost engines with their thrust augmented by water injection was such that the extra assisted take-off potential was not required. Development continued, however, with a Ministry contract covering eight engines and the Sprite was fired nearly 500 times and 30 take-offs made in the Comet. Substitution of silver gauze catalyst packs in the chamber eased injection complications and gave a clean exhaust.

The Super Sprite engine first ran in April 1953 and was a hot unit with kerosene injection and combustion chamber throat cooling designed to give 4,200lb thrust for 40 seconds, two units meeting the tropical take-off case for the Vickers Valiant bomber. In September 1954 the Super Sprite became the first rocket engine to gain Air Ministry type approval and the unit then went into production. One hundred and sixty six were produced in a nacelle configuration to be jettisoned from the Valiant after take-off. Recovery was by parachute and the landing was cushioned by air bags.

The Spectre

In 1952 rig testing commenced on components for a turbopump-fed controllable-thrust rocket engine primarily for installation in high altitude fighter aircraft. The engine was designed for 8,000lb thrust and to be throttled to 20% of this figure in flight operation. The design was compact at 610lb weight with its turbopump discharging into the combustion chamber upstream of the fuel injection burner. The engine first ran in its cold configuration in July 1953, with peroxide cooling in autumn 1954, and to full temperature and thrust in summer 1955. It was cleared for flight in November 1956 with controllable thrust level between 2,000 and 7,000lb. Flight trials commenced in a modified Canberra bomber in December 1956.

Lancastrian taking off from Hatfield in 1947 with Ghost engines and a trials installation of the German wartime Walter 109/500 rocket assisted take off units.

Sprite rocket engine on its test bed in the early 1950s with members of the special projects department, W N Neat, A V Cleaver, R A Grimston and E Dove. Val Cleaver led this enthusiastic group and subsequently transferred to Derby and Spadeadam.

Comet 1 prototype take off from Hatfield on one of the 30 trials made with rocket assistance.

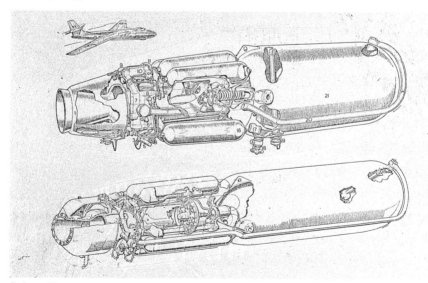

Sprite 'cold' unit of 1949 and the Super Sprite 'hot' assisted take-off rocket unit of 1953.

Port side view of the Spectre D.Spe.1.

Spectre engine on test in silenced test bed with water cooled exhaust silencing arrangements.

Night trials on the Spectre in its second Canberra flight test conversion.

The Spectre running at Hatfield on Test in a trial SR53 rear fuselage.

78

SR53 prepared for ground running at Boscombe Down in 1958.

SR53 cleared for flight at Boscombe Down.

SR53 at altitude.

Handley Page Victor undertaking its trial take off with Spectre A T O units from the Hatfield runway.

First application of the engine was to be the Saunders Roe SR53 mixed-power high performance research aircraft. The aircraft flew on 16 May 1957 and was joined by a second aircraft as flight development proceeded. In October 1957 a contract for the considerably developed version, the SR177, was announced. This was to incorporate the Gyron PS 50 engine at 14,000lb combat thrust to give full mixed-power interceptor capability.

This period, however, followed the notorious 1957 White Paper and was an era of uncertainty. On 15 June 1958 Saunders Roe's Chief Test Pilot, Sqdn. Ldr. John Booth, was killed in a take-off accident to the second prototype SR53 at Boscombe Down. No fault was ascribed to the engine or the HTP feature of the aeroplane although no cause was published. It appeared to be a case of an aborted take-off turned to tragedy by subsequent overrun of the runway into obstacles beyond.

No further flight testing was undertaken with the SR53 and whilst construction of the SR177 was almost completed, with the incentive of a German Navy order, the programme was terminated in common with virtually all the other British manned military aircraft projects of the period.

Development of the Spectre continued into 1959 with Spectre 4 as an assisted take-off unit and the Spectre 5 as a controllable-thrust unit. The Spectre 4 weighed 380lb with a control system for fixed thrust at 8,000lb and duration up to some 40 seconds, limited by its nacelle tankage. Application was intended to both the Victor and Vulcan bombers. In the event, although the engine and its nacelle went into production, circumstances changed with requirements for V-bomber operation virtually limited to UK bases and only one single trial take-off was undertaken with a Victor.

Final application of the de Havilland rocket engines was to the early development rounds of the Avro Blue Steel flying stand-off bomb which was subsequently carried

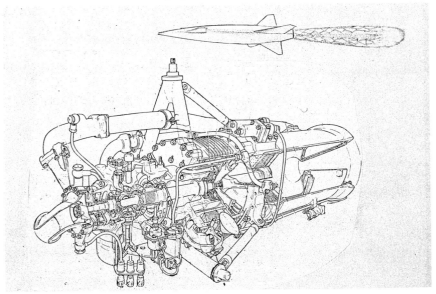

Sectioned view of Spectre engine.

81

in service by the Avro Vulcan. In this application a fixed thrust Spectre 4 was mounted above a Spectre 5 to provide a powerplant with 16,000lb thrust for launch, and controllable down to 1,000lb or so for cruise. The Blue Steel flew for the first time powered by this unit in October 1959.

APU and Peroxide Starter

In the latter phase of rocket development work, the use of HTP with aircraft and missile accessories was developed. An auxiliary power unit was produced initially as an ingenious update of the classical 'Hero' turbine with HTP fed to the centre of a rotating wheel containing a catalyst pack, with the resulting steam discharging through peripheral nozzles. Control proved difficult and development was then directed to a conventional impulse turbine with a peroxide pump arranged on the common shaft and feeding via the catalyst pack to a conventional partial-admission nozzle system.

A diminutive unit resulted weighing 25lb with power options between 25 and 50hp at 33,000rpm, with a consumption at the 25hp case of approximately 9lb per minute. The unit was extensively tested in configurations mounted on auxiliary gearboxes so

Twin Spectre for Blue Steel missile development in 1949 at full thrust on test at Hatfield.

82

25hp H T P powered auxiliary power unit for the production round of the Blue Steel stand-off missile.

Peroxide Starter for Gyron Junior PS50 in SR177.

that, when main power was available from the aircraft's turbojet engine it was driven, and with loss of power the unit was peroxide fed and became the sustainer. Extensive development work was done for the SR53 application and intended for the SR177. The unit then went into limited production as the main accessory drive unit for the Blue Steel stand-off bomb.

Pre-dating these developments and extending HTP design practice to the jet propulsion engine team, an HTP starter was developed. Again this was a simple unit, feeding peroxide to a catalyst pack from an external ground support trolley. The resulting steam flow then drove at 40,000rpm a 4⅝ in diameter turbine geared to the jet engine rotor through its starting sequence via a conventional free-wheel system. Approximately 11lb of HTP were used for a start on the Gyron engine. These starts were extremely impressive. With electric starting the high inertia of the large Gyron engine dictated 30 second start time whilst, with the peroxide starter, 10 seconds was achieved. The unit was mounted in the intake bullet with the resulting steam output exhausting free into the engine intake zone. This feature at test always gave a very dramatic impression with the initial cloud of steam being quickly swept into the intake as the engine accelerated.

Wider applications of the starter were visualised with the ability to operate on compressed air and in the SR177 of course, it would have provided, together with the APU, total DH supply for all power requirements.

Chapter 7
THE NUCLEAR POWER GROUP

The de Havilland Engine Company first established an interest in nuclear power developments in 1954 when specialist staff were attached to the Atomic Energy Research Establishment at Harwell to examine the possibility of utilising this new form of energy for propulsion purposes. A major part of their task concerned investigation of certain types of small, highly-rated systems from which important conclusions were reached concerning the possibilities of the high temperature gas-cooled reactor (HTGCR). Acting on this conclusion the Company established a team of technologists, known as the Nuclear Power Group, comprising technical, drawing office and experimental sections, with the object of making a practical contribution to the official programme of research concerned with the development of the HTGCR.

Typical of the activities of the Group in this respect were the design and construction of a high temperature gas-cooled loop for testing new types of ceramic fuel elements in the Pluto research reactor at Harwell. In this same connection the Group undertook research on the thermal shock resistance properties of ceramics. From its work on the loop, the Group developed items of equipment as standard commercial products. These included small high-speed gas circulators incorporating self-acting gas bearings, and a series of small valves, all of which met the exacting requirements for radioactive gas circuits. Design studies were also undertaken for the Admiralty of a 50,000hp twin reactor HTGC system for marine propulsion purposes. The Group participated in the Advanced Gas Cooled Reactor programme (AGR) with the design and construction of the primary gas circuit equipment for the Hero reactor at Windscale. The group was wound up following incorporation into Bristol Siddeley.

Chapter 8
GAS TURBINE POWER FOR HELICOPTERS
& GENERAL AVIATION

With the loss of all the military contracts following the 1957 White Paper, prospects changed dramatically in the succeeding year. This could not be viewed as a temporary setback against ongoing logical development but as the cessation of all future requirements for military combat aircraft. Subsequent events of course proved otherwise.

A new market sector had therefore to be found and this was emergent in the application of gas turbine engines to the power range of 750 to 2,000hp. Below this range the piston engine was, and is still, firmly entrenched as a consequence of simplicity, low cost and fuel consumption. In comparison the problems presented to gas turbine design in small units requires ultra-high speed, small component size &

1958 the year of transition. Following the 1957 Government White Paper proposing no future military front line aircraft, the axed Gyron Senior compares with the GE T58 helicopter engine, symbolising the new product field.

86

fine clearances. The helicopter case, where the obvious key benefit of low power-plant weight permits penetration into the domain of the piston engine, was calculated as giving the greatest growth potential in terms of annual sales.

In 1955 a design had been prepared for a two-spool turboshaft engine of 1200hp designated as the PS57. This had a low pressure shaft with a five-stage axial compressor and two-stage turbine providing the output power and a separate high pressure assembly of a centrifugal compressor driven by its own turbine. No development contract was forthcoming for this project however and since the company had other commitments the proposal was dropped.

The Gnome

In early 1958 the company capitalised on a mutual assistance agreement it had held since 1951 with the General Electric company of America to take out a licence for the European manufacture of the T58 helicopter turboshaft engine. This had been developed under a US Naval contract and had reached US type test standard in the autumn of 1957. The engine featured a sophisticated ten-stage axial compressor with the GE feature of variable inlet guide vanes on three stator rows. This gave stable operation over the required wide running range without the need for the wasteful air bleed normally associated with the achieved compression ratio of 8.3 to 1. Resultant engine cruise fuel consumption was at 0.67lb/shp/hr. The compressor was driven by a two-stage turbine at 26,000rpm fed via an annular combustion chamber. Output power was extracted by a single-stage turbine at 19,500rpm giving, with these early

An early Gnome installation check in the Whirlwind conversion at Westlands.

engines, 1,000hp. Power-to-weight ratio was at 2.86 to 1 compared to the classic developed piston engine figure of 1 to 1.

The T58 as originally licenced ran on test at the Hatfield Test Site in August 1958 and flew in a Westland Whirlwind helicopter in March 1959. The licence assumed anglicisation of the engine and the engine proper was redrawn to utilise British materials. A new fuel system was designed by Lucas in conjunction with the de Havilland Propeller Co. to give electronic control. A new design of output gearbox was provided instead of plain bearings featuring ball and roller bearings and with an integral torquemeter sensing the separating loads on the twin helical gears incorporated. The engine was named 'Gnome' and ran in its anglicised form in June 1959 with production committed from that date. It first flew in August 1959 in the Whirlwind, and in May 1960 a trial installation flew in a Westland Wasp.

In 1961 a coupled-twin engine was run for the Westland Wessex helicopter, the engine was uprated to 1200hp, and programmes were initiated to power the European variants of the Agusta Bell 204 and 205, Vertol 107, and Sikorsky S61. Agusta in Italy designed their new three-engined Agusta 101 helicopter on the basis of Gnome engines and the engine was projected for various hovercraft applications. In September 1960 a turboprop variant of the engine ran on the de Havilland Propeller Co's large hangar test bed sited adjacent to the Engine Company site at Hatfield and various general aviation and V/STOL applications were planned.

Gnome Production Test Bed at Leavesden.

The prototype Gnome P1200 Turboprop.

Chapter 9
PEOPLE & PREMISES

People

The decade centred on 1960 must be viewed at all levels as a major industrial watershed, certainly equalling in its effects the changes and consequences of the two world wars. From the viewpoint of the aviation industry transition was to that of aerospace, and with international developments in electronics and computerisation, the dawn of the second industrial revolution. The aerospace industry in the United Kingdom condensed into single units with regard to airframe and engines and this process was hastened for the de Havilland grouping as a consequence of the Comet disasters, followed by the implications of the 1957 White Paper on Defence.

The period of the mid- to late-fifties represented the apogee of the de Havilland Engine Company with regard to organisational and product diversity, and Company profitability and employment. Production rates had peaked in the early 1950s at the period of the Korean War which had re-awakened the need for armaments following the hopeful period of the early post-war years. Leavesden had become the Head Office of the Company in March 1954 with production and business departments located there; Stag Lane was now the engineering division; and Hatfield the test and research area. The factory at Stonegrove, Edgware, was closed and razed to the ground in deference to its wartime antecedents of construction on green belt land

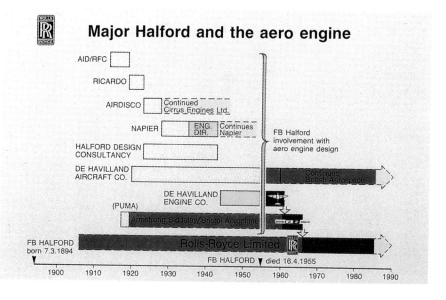

Major Halford and the aero engine

F B Halford in maturity.

In 1955 Major Halford died at the age of 61 at which time he was Chairman and Technical Director of the Company, and in 1959 his long-term associate, J L P Brodie, Engineering Director, also died. Their colleagues from the pre-war pioneering team were approaching retirement and those that had joined the wartime expansion of the industry were now mature. Dr ES Moult of the original consultancy design team, having succeeded them in the technical.directorate, continued into a later era perpetuating the spirit and qualities of the organisation.

Sir Geoffrey de Havilland addressing an annual supervisory staff association dinner at Leavesden.

Dr E S Moult in his office at Stag Lane.

In 1957, the year of the Government White Paper, employment had peaked at approximately 6,300 people. The Board at that time was supported by Sir Geoffrey de Havilland as President, A F Burke as Chairman, H Buckingham as General Manager, and W E Nixon, all long-term associates of de Havilland, who were also directors of the Aircraft Co. J L P Brodie, Dr E S Moult and M G Ash completed the Board.

The 6,300 employees of the company comprised approximately 2,750 works personnel, divided equally between those directly associated with engine production and those tradesmen supporting them. Some 2,500 people undertook staff and technical jobs and 350 management, supervision and senior technical specialisation. Approximately 700 apprentices were under training, which can be considered as an exceptional proportionate holding and a very positive index of the prospects for expansion viewed at that time.

I T has long been felt in certain quarters of the de Havilland Engine Company that the scope of the market for its many products can never be fully realised while the pinch-penny attitude of aircraft designers towards engines is allowed to continue. These guilty men, in spite of the miraculous achievements of engine designers in reducing to near impercepti-bility the dimensions and consumption of their products, are prepared to suffer only one, two, three, or, in very favoured circumstances, four power units to each of their universally over-bodied and underpowered aircraft. To satisfy this long-felt want, the Engine Company has gathered to itself a well-knit team of dis-gruntled " body builders " who have put their heart and soul into producing a truly marvel-lous and outstanding machine more in keeping with a progressive engine sales policy. Aimed at showing the airframe people some of the more obvious lessons to be learnt from their own niggardliness, the new aircraft, named the Powerplantation, has been " destretched " from the outset to allow for the traditional extension of the fuselage as its various engines are developed to achieve higher and higher outputs in the normal fashion. The current derated version of the Powerplantation is powered by (from inboard to outboard) two de Havilland Gyron Junior turbojets with reheat, two Super Sprite A.T.O. rockets, two Gnome turboprops, and two Gipsy Queen 70 and Major 10 piston engines. Atop the fuselage are two Gnome turboshaft units and in the tail a Double Spectre rocket. Other leading aero-engine manufacturers are already clamouring for the drawings of this brilliant conception by the Company's technical sales department and negotiations are well advanced for the Power-plantation to be built under licence at Derby, Filton, Cincinatti and Connecticut.

The Engine Man's Dreamboat

Pride Goeth before a Fall – Brockbank cartoon and text from DH Gazette.

In 1960 de Havilland Holdings Ltd. was acquired by the Hawker Siddeley Group Ltd. This was the year of the 50th anniversary of Geoffrey de Havilland's first flight in his own aircraft, with an engine of his own design, and the 40th anniversary of the founding of the de Havilland Aircraft Co. The de Havilland Engine Co. did in fact perpetuate the name until August 1962 when the reorganisation of Hawker Siddeley was completed. This included integration of both the de Havilland Engine Co. and Blackburn Engines Ltd, old rivals, into Bristol Siddeley Engines Ltd., thus complet-ing the merger process begun in 1959 when Bristol's engine interests were combined with Armstrong Siddeley Ltd.

The general manpower structure of employment in an aircraft engine firm makes an instructive comparison with that of an 'average' engineering company as revealed in Engineering Industry Training Board statistics for the mid-1960s:

	Percentage of employees Aircraft engineering	'Average' engineering
Semi- and unskilled	13	31
Skilled	28	21
Technician	16	7
Technologist	4	2
Admin. & Clerical	20	16
Managers & supervision	6	7.5
Others	13	15.5

At this time approximately 5,500 people were in employment; 3,600 at Leavesden, 400 at Hatfield and 1,500 at Stag Lane.

Training

The history of training arrangements within a company provides an interesting indicator of style and fortune. From its beginning de Havillands had recruited apprentices to meet the nucleus of its needs for specialist skilled craftsmen and, from this stream, its draughtsmen and some of its engineers.

Reflecting its strong association with the expanding civil aviation field, from 1928 student apprenticeships were offered for the 18 to 25 age group at a premium of 350

Apprentice interview of the 1950s. An aspiring engineer and supportive mother with Squadron Leader Reeve of the de Havilland Aeronautical Technical School.

95

guineas for a three year course. Matriculation in at least four subjects was required with credits in maths and a foreign language. This was outward-looking training aimed at aircraft and engine operation and it laid the foundation for fruitful long-term associations in attracting middle-class British and foreign students. Amy Johnson, a Stag Lane ground engineering student, could be considered as representative in style, if not in sex, of the training scheme output and N S Norway, perhaps better known as the author Neville Shute, was an excellent publicist for the de Havilland Aeronautical Technical School as it became known in the 1930s.

In 1937 the craft apprenticeship scheme, which assumed joining the Company on leaving school at 14 and then time-serving for 5 years from 16 to 21, became more sophisticated. The opportunity was provided for day release to Willesden Technical College to study for a specially-structured Ordinary National Certificate Course, with the unusual Company insistence that the first year syllabus include English and current affairs.

This system continued throughout the war. At the end of the war all apprentices commenced their training with up to the first year completed 'off the job' in the training school. This was a pioneer example of the practice subsequently made national, post-1966, by the Training Boards. In 1948 City & Guilds Craft courses were introduced to meet the needs of craft apprentices since failure rates on the professional institutions National Certificate courses were running in this post-war phase at 65%. Through the 1950s the premium student apprenticeships phased out. The pattern of apprenticeships stabilised, with a 5/4 year craft stream studying C & G

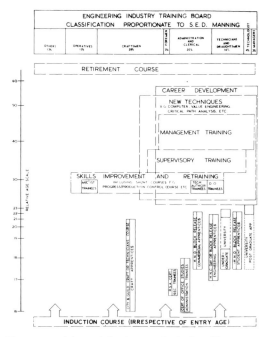

Chart summarising Manpower training and development in the late 60s, post creation of the National Training Boards.

or ONC courses, and engineering apprentices post-GCE A-level entry, or upgraded post-ONC level studying to HNC, and latterly HND level. Some scholarships were offered and both undergraduate and post-graduate apprenticeships.

An interesting sidelight from the 1949 prospectus, which now has an oddly old-fashioned ring, refers to the educational needs of school leavers at 15 "to be encouraged to prepare for apprenticeship by taking continual classes in general subjects and then to continue the general subjects while steadily initiating the apprentice's aeronautical studies. It is useless filling boys heads with technicalities until the basic education has taken root. They must learn about their country and their industry, acquire a pride in work and appreciate where they are heading."

Premises

Since 1954 Leavesden, with its aerodrome site and two major factory complexes, has been the major activity centre.

The Stag Lane works had been the centre of all de Havilland activities from 1920 to 1932 and subsequently, with the closure of the aerodrome, changed its role initially to engine and propeller work and then from the end of the 1939-45 war concentrated on engine design and development. In 1967 this work transferred to Leavesden and for a short period Stag Lane continued as a factory satellite to the Bristol company facilities on Olympus engine work for Concorde before finally closing in 1971.

Premises at Hatfield, on the remote side of the aerodrome, were first operated early in the war for Merlin engine hangar testing, with the engine and propeller

The Stonegrove Goblin and Ghost engine factory at Stanmore in the 1950s.

97

The Stag Lane works in the 1950s, the aerodrome now a dream of the past.

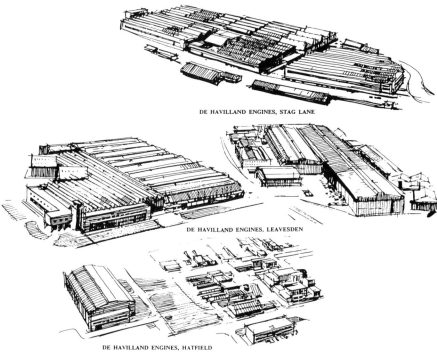

DE HAVILLAND ENGINES, STAG LANE

DE HAVILLAND ENGINES, LEAVESDEN

DE HAVILLAND ENGINES, HATFIELD

Premises of the de Havilland Engine Company circa 1960.

John Young's impression of Hatfield circa 1960 as re-produced in the contemporary de Havilland Gazette.

combination, the remote site being a requirement for continuous engine test operation. Napiers maintained association with hangar test beds sited, and independently managed, between the de Havilland Propeller and Engine Company's test areas at Hatfield. Gas turbine engine testing commenced with the Goblin in 1942 and subsequently numbers of test beds were built culminating in Test Bed No.25 in 1954. This allowed fully-silenced testing of the massive Gyron jet engine, then the largest and most powerful engine in the world.

A major investment in facilities was concentrated in the Gas Dynamics Laboratory initially built in 1947 for combustion and aerodynamic research and then expanded as the 'Halford Laboratory' from 1952. The largest laboratory facility is the 18,000hp compressor test rig, the power for which is derived from what is, in effect, a Comet 1 powerplant installation of four 5,000lb thrust Ghost engines with their exhausts

Compressor plant at the Halford Lab. at Hatfield with Pegasus compressor under installation for test.

directed to power turbines each developing 4,500hp and arranged as twin tandem units.

This facility, originally designed to drive and test the Gyron engine series compressors, has continued in use in testing the compressors of engines from the Bristol and Derby design departments with particular emphasis on the Olympus and Pegasus engine units. It has only recently, 25 years after its initial commissioning, been superseded as the Company's major facility of its type.

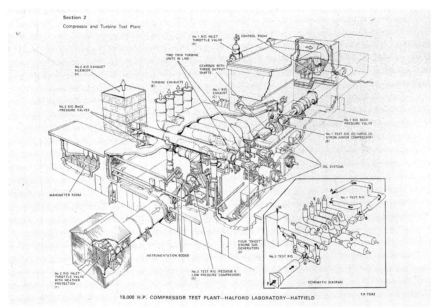

The 18,000hp compressor plant in the Halford Lab. at Hatfield. Virtually a Comet 1 power installation harnessed to industrial type power turbine units. In operation from the 1950s to the early 1980s as the company's most powerful compressor test plant.

Chapter 10
LEAVESDEN

Leavesden was a small village on the road from Watford to Abbots Langley and beyond to Hemel Hempstead and has been given a national and latterly international significance by a paradox of its location. On one scale it lies in the belt of home counties countryside just clear of London and on a lesser scale on the rural district boundary of Watford. In 1869 a major hospital was built on the northern outskirts of the village as a consequence of the policy to site satellite mental asylums around London. In the 1930s urbanisation of London forced circumstances for the transfer of manufacturers aerodromes into the same belt of countryside. de Havilland Aircraft Co. Ltd. and Handley Page Ltd. moved respectively from Edgware to Hatfield and from Cricklewood to Radlett.

In 1937 former farmland to the west of Leavesden was purchased by the Watford Borough Council and this 117 acres was designated as the seventh of Watford's recreation grounds and named as the King George V Recreation Ground. The western boundary of this area was defined by the cuttings and tunnels of the LMS

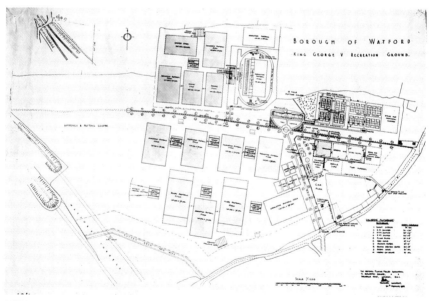

1937 intent. The Borough of Watford's ambitious plan for a King George V recreation ground initiated but overtaken by wartime aerodrome construction on the site in the vicinity of Leavesden village.

Railway, formerly the London to Birmingham Railway of George Stephenson. The tunnel, initially single, was a pioneer example 1 mile and 170 yards long opened in 1837 after the loss of ten lives in its excavation.

With the outbreak of war in 1939 the predominant industrial activity of Hertfordshire became aircraft manufacture. Handley Page with its aerodrome at Radlett and factories in North London was manufacturing Hampden bombers and developing its major wartime product, the four-engined Halifax bomber. de Havilland at Hatfield was producing training and communications aircraft including the Oxford and Tiger Moth types. The Mosquito design was in gestation.

In late 1940 the Ministry of Aircraft Production instructed the de Havilland Aircraft Company to investigate the manufacture of Vickers Wellington twin-engined bombers and this presupposed the construction of new factories and the provision of a parallel organisation. Surveys were flown to determine a suitable site for a shadow factory and aerodrome. Leavesden became the obvious choice as a flat area of non-agricultural land adjacent to a centre of population offering employment potential and with excellent road communications. The Air Ministry acquired the land by compulsory purchase on behalf of the Ministry of Aircraft Production and began immediate construction of the aerodrome and factory provisions.

Views of Leavesden in 1943 with some of the 1,390 Mosquitos produced on assembly at the L.2 factory.

A 1,000yd runway, 150ft wide, aligned on the prevailing west-south-west wind was constructed, along with two separate factory areas to the north of the runway towards Kings Langley, one adjacent to Leavesden village and the other half mile to the west. This latter was dubbed No 1 factory and both were connected to the runway by taxi tracks allowing convenient access and take-off for lightly-loaded aircraft. A number of ground running sheds were provided adjacent to the factory areas and flight clearance and rectification sheds were provided – one adjacent to the normal take-off end and the major shed at the remote end of the runway conveniently placed for reception of aircraft after flight test. In the event, the de Havilland programme for production of Wellington bombers lapsed when contracts for Mosquito were placed and plans were then pursued for the manufacture of the Mosquito and the Handley Page Halifax.

The de Havilland Aircraft Company formed the Second Aircraft Group with a Mosquito production organisation centred on the Leavesden No 2 factory, drawing major sub-assemblies from factories established around the county and completing these by final assembly, flight clearance, test and delivery. Prior to the programme proper commencing, records state that 140 sets of components for the Oxford aircraft, designed by the then subsidiary company of Airspeed Ltd., together with 60 fuselages and 147 wings, were produced. Mosquito production then got under way with 53 aircraft completed in 1942, 379 in 1943, 585 in 1944 and 373 to August 15, VJ Day, giving wartime production of 1,390.

Mosquitos and Merlins.

Lunch time activities at leavesden in 1943.

At the Leavesden No. 1 factory was centred a separate and major aircraft activity in an organisation managed by London Transport Ltd and known as the London Aircraft Production Group. Management and production responsibility was independent of the aircraft parent company at Cricklewood and Radlett and, as with the Mosquito, major components flowed to the factory for completion and flight test from factories primarily in the North West London area, with strong contribution from bus maintenance depots including Aldenham. Napiers also used the Aldenham depot as a base for Sabre production hangar test facilities to allow these noisy operations to be avoided at their Acton works.

Two variants of the Halifax bomber were produced, initiated by the Halifax II with Rolls-Royce Merlin XX engines, and the first aircraft of a total production of 450 of this type flew from the site on 8 December 1941. From 1943 production was centred on the Halifax B3 powered by the Bristol Hercules radial engine. 260 aircraft of this mark were completed and the last aircraft, the 710th, flew out on 16 April 1945.

This aircraft activity was a major and probably under-appreciated contribution to the war effort. Halifax work terminated rapidly at war's end with cancellation of an outstanding contract for 120 aircraft but Mosquito activity, now under responsibility of de Havilland Aircraft, continued in low key for approximately two years after the war, with considerable numbers of aircraft in evidence around the boundary of the airfield.

The last de Havilland Aircraft activity to be completed on site was in the early 1950s when a batch of Vampire aircraft were converted at the No. 2 factory. This was for the rubber mat recovery-at-sea exercises pursued by the Fleet Air Arm as a follow-up to the wartime activity which catapulted Hurricane and other fighter aircraft off merchantmen in convoys for defence. This update of procedures was planned to allow recovery of aircraft and pilots rather than the parachuting or ditching wartime solution. Also at this time, with Vampire and Venom jet fighter production at peak at Hatfield for the considerable export activity, the No. 1 Flight Shed at the remote runway end was used as an aircraft clearance and final flight test satellite.

All of the wartime activities paved the way for the subsequent use of the aerodrome and site. The LAP group activity at Leavesden No. 1 factory was terminated,

Halifax role-out at Leavesden 1, an occasion with Military band in attendance.

106

Conversion of Vampires at Leavesden for rubber deck landing flight trials in the early 1950s.

leaving the premises empty on a care and maintenance basis, and the de Havilland Aircraft Company was working at a low key in No. 2 factory. In the war years there had been strong aircraft engine associations with some 4,600 Rolls-Royce Merlin engines and 1,040 Bristol Hercules flying off from the aerodrome.

Thus, in 1945 the situation was that there were large factory premises available with a de Havilland Aircraft Company presence on site. Progressive transfer of the Engine Company's facilities commenced initially with Gipsy work from the Edgware shadow subsidiary factories then subsequently the jet propulsion engine work from the major wartime factory at Stonegrove, and eventually with the transfer and sale of the original de Havilland factory and office premises at Stag Lane.

Chapter 11
BRISTOL SIDDELEY ENGINES LTD

From November 1961 the de Havilland Engine Co. became part of Bristol Siddeley Engines and in August 1962 ceased to trade under its former name.

By 1964 all of the small gas turbine and piston engine activities formerly undertaken by the constituent companies which made up Bristol Siddeley Engines, i.e. Bristol Aero-Engines, Armstrong Siddeley and Blackburn Engines, were concentrated at the former de Havilland works. This meant in effect the transfer of the Blackburn engines from Brough, after a brief sojourn at Bristol and Coventry, and discontinuance of competitive work at Coventry.

Since 1952 Blackburn Engines Ltd. had been producing engines based on French Turbomeca designs. Three were auxiliary power-plants. The Palouste was primarily a ground unit producing compressed air at 54lb/sq.in at flows to 2.3lb/second for starting turbojet engines in RAF and RN service, and the Artouste and Cumulus were derivatives uprated to provide in addition shaft power for electrical generation at 100hp. The Artouste was the established military airborne auxiliary power plant and continued in service into the '70s although its installation in the Trident 1E airliner could not be considered a success. It was subsequently phased out. Development of the Cumulus was terminated soon after becoming a Leavesden responsibility when the TSR-2, its primary application, was cancelled.

The fourth engine to be transferred of Blackburn origin was the Nimbus helicopter engine which powers the Westland Scout for the Army and the Wasp for the Navy. These aircraft are very much the workhorses for their respective Services and they and their engines are required to give robust service. The engine has been in service since 1963. Whilst having a maximum power of 1050hp it is flat-rated for 1 hour at 685hp, this power being available to 9,200ft for altitude conditions relevant to Army operation, and to sea level ambient temperatures of International Standard + 25°C relevant to naval applications.

The Gnome engine became a great success in powering the Whirlwind, Agusta Bell 204, Wessex, Sea King, Vertol 107, and Commando helicopters, and the SRN3, 5 and 6 hovercraft. Power ratings have increased by various steps of development from the initial 1,000hp of the H1000 engines to the 1,540hp of the current production H1400-1 engines. In 1966 a 1,800hp variant was run with a two-stage power turbine but this was not proceeded with. Its development was continued in the USA with testing at 1,960hp. 2200 engines had been produced to the end of 1986 and the engine will almost certainly continue in production into the 1990s.

The Gnome turboshaft and its application.

Gnome powered Sea Kings, a classic rescue scene.

Chapter 12
ROLLS-ROYCE LIMITED – SMALL ENGINE DIVISION

In October 1966 Rolls-Royce Limited took over Bristol Siddeley Engines and the Leavesden operation became the Small Engine Division, placing the organisation as part of one of the world's three major aircraft engine companies.

In March 1967 a memorandum of understanding was signed between the French and British Governments for the joint production of three helicopter types and their engines to meet requirements of their armed forces. The first two aircraft were of French design, the Aerospatiale Puma assault helicopter and Gazelle light observation helicopter with their respective Turbomeca powerplants Turmo III C4 and Astazou IIN2. The third aircraft was the Westland WG13 Lynx utility helicopter with its BS360 engine.

Since this was to be a collaborative design and manufacture project overall, and the two French aircraft were at an advanced state of development, the design work on the Lynx and its engine would be predominantly British.

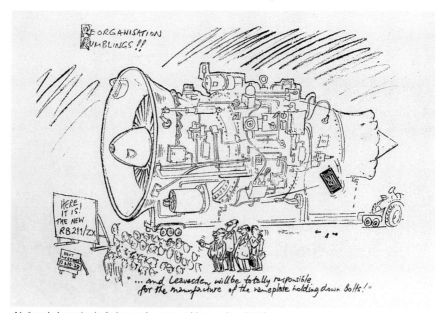

Unfounded worries in facing a take-over and integration situation

Manufacturing work on all three types would be shared on the basis of numbers needed by the relevant services of the two partners. Thus there would be an almost immediate work build-up on the Leavesden manufacturing shops to satisfy Turmo and Astazou production, with the subsequent opportunity to bid for spares and overhaul work. This would be followed by development, production and support work on the BS360 engine now named 'Gem'.

The Gem Engine

In November 1966 submissions had been made to the Ministry of Defence for a new helicopter engine to be designed and manufactured at Leavesden.

At the project stage, two alternatives were offered. One placed emphasis on a simple configuration similar to a Gnome type engine but using high technology design for its compressor. This would give a lightweight unit but with relatively high fuel consumption. As an alternative proposal a two-spool high-economy engine was projected with a four-stage axial low pressure compressor followed by a centrifugal high pressure compressor; each unit being driven by its own turbine and with power then extracted by an additional two-stage turbine. The low pressure compressor, being limited to four stages, would require no variable angle stator blades or bleed and the centrifugal compressor represented the logical solution for the high pressure stage where an axial unit would impose such small size on blades as to be impractical.

In May 1967, with the Anglo-French agreement signed and the Lynx requirement confirmed, finalised proposals were made for the engine, which followed the earlier high-efficiency proposal of a fairly complex engine giving low fuel consumption. The

The Gem and its various applications.

111

engine was to incorporate a four-stage compressor running at 36,650rpm and high pressure centrifugal compressor running at 40,000rpm with the output power turbine running at 27,000rpm and geared down to what has become the standard gas turbine helicopter transmission speed of 6,000rpm. Maximum power rating was at 830hp with maximum contingency power at 900hp with a specific fuel consumption at design point of .489lb/hp/hr.

In August 1967 the engineering department moved from the Stag Lane factory to Leavesden and thus finally severed connections with Edgware. All effort was now concentrated at Leavesden and in September 1967, with a design organisation established in the new offices, detailed design work was initiated for the new engine.

In July 1969 the engine gas generator section was run, followed in September by the running of the prototype engine. In September 1970 ground running commenced at Westlands on a rotor rig.

Thus, at this time, the Small Engine Division had busy manufacturing shops with high throughput of Gnome engines supplemented by work on the ex-Blackburn Nimbus, Artouste and Palouste engines and some residual work on the apparently ever-lasting Gipsy engines. Production of the BS360 was planned, speeded by the fact that experimental engines were to be produced on production tooling. In addition, planning was proceeding for the more-immediate flow to the shops of work on the French Astazou and Turmo engines against the overall agreement. These requirements to be centred mainly on the manufacture of engine non-rotatives embracing hot end components, intake casings, and gear trains.

In February 1971 Rolls-Royce Limited became bankrupt as a consequence of the development costs of the large RB211 engine for the TriStar and implications of a fixed price contract with changing dollar values. In May 1971 a new company, Rolls-Royce (1971) Limited, emerged from the receivership. In March 1971 the Westland WG13 Lynx flew for the first time. It performed well from its inception with its two BS360 engines and the Leavesden operation was thus able to demonstrate, in very positive terms, its viability.

In February 1972 the BS360 passed its 150 hour type approval test. From August 1973 the basic production type, designated and named 'Gem', passed through its bench and flight testing phase with the Lynx, a combination of new airframe and new engine. From December 1975 production deliveries commenced of the Gem 2 with a max. contingency power at 900shp and max. continuous at 750shp. In subsequent years development and production of the engine has proceeded with of the order of 1,000 engines delivered to 1986. Various upratings have been pursued for improvement in performance and reliability. This relates to the subtle variation demanded in world-wide helicopter operation consequent on varying climatic and altitude conditions.

A growth version of the engine, Gem 41, went into service in 1979 in uprated versions of the naval Lynx and in the Westland W30. The latest growth stage is the Gem 60 with a compressor pressure ratio of 14 to 1, power uprated to 1203shp, and with digital electronic control. This major variant first ran in December 1981 for further developments of the Lynx and for the civil and military versions of the Westland 30.

In August 1986 a Gem 60 powered Westland Company demonstrator Army Lynx, G-LYNX, modified to accept Westland's new BERP rotor concept allowing near supersonic tip speed and a 40% increase in performance, set a new world speed record for helicopters at a speed of 400.87kph/249.10mph.

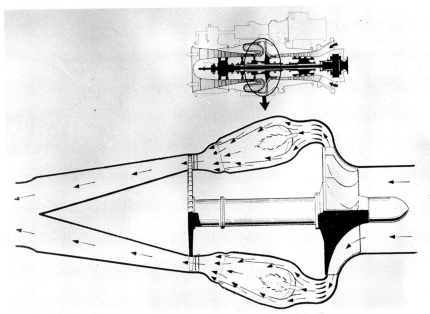

Contrast in complexity and size. Ghost rotatives compared with those of the Gem.

PISTON ENGINE POWERED

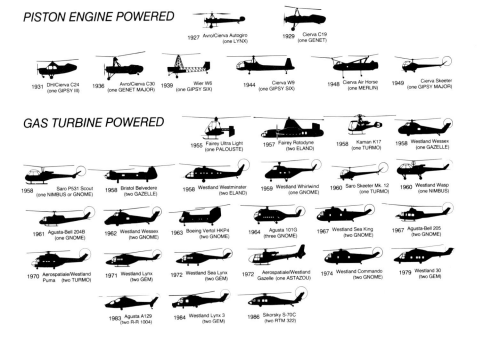

1927 Avro/Cierva Autogiro (one LYNX)

1929 Cierva C19 (one GENET)

1931 DH/Cierva C24 (one GIPSY III)

1936 Avro/Cierva C30 (one GENET MAJOR)

1939 Wier W6 (one GIPSY SIX)

1944 Cierva W9 (one GIPSY SIX)

1948 Cierva Air Horse (one MERLIN)

1949 Cierva Skeeter (one GIPSY MAJOR)

GAS TURBINE POWERED

1955 Fairey Ultra Light (one PALOUSTE)

1957 Fairey Rotodyne (two ELAND)

1958 Kaman K17 (one TURMO)

1958 Westland Wessex (one GAZELLE)

1958 Saro P531 Scout (one NIMBUS or GNOME)

1958 Bristol Belvedere (two GAZELLE)

1958 Westland Westminster (two ELAND)

1959 Westland Whirlwind (one GNOME)

1960 Saro Skeeter Mk. 12 (one TURMO)

1960 Westland Wasp (one NIMBUS)

1961 Agusta-Bell 204B (one GNOME)

1962 Westland Wessex (two GNOME)

1963 Boeing Vertol HKP4 (two GNOME)

1964 Agusta 101G (three GNOME)

1967 Westland Sea King (two GNOME)

1967 Agusta-Bell 205 (two GNOME)

1970 Aerospatiale/Westland Puma (two TURMO)

1971 Westland Lynx (two GEM)

1972 Westland Sea Lynx (two GEM)

1972 Aerospatiale/Westland Gazelle (one ASTAZOU)

1974 Westland Commando (two GNOME)

1979 Westland 30 (two GEM)

1983 Agusta A129 (two R-R 1004)

1984 Westland Lynx 3 (two GEM)

1986 Sikorsky S-70C (two RTM 322)

113

Gem
Production

An intensive engine development programme had been undertaken to increase power exceeding the torque limit of the rotor transmission requiring at the engine maximum contingency rating 1249hp per engine. With water methanol injection at the engine intake, and at sea level standard conditions/planned flight speed, engine power available was projected as at 1600hp, a considerable excess on the permissible rotor demand. This prospect of surplus power led to consideration in trading this off against the potential for jet thrust in directing reduced area engine exhaust pipes to

No.2 Factory

No.1 Factory

L922

Leavesden's factories and aerodrome.

114

the rear, thus producing a direct propulsive force supplementing that as normally derived from the aircraft's rotor. Experimentation on the test bed and on the airframe installation determined that with a near 60% reduction in exhaust nozzle area, 390lb of thrust per engine resulted at maximum contingency temperature and at the transmission torque limit. The Westland paper on the speed record endeavour records final matching of the port and starboard installations with hacksaw adjustments to the exhausts!

Another interesting variant of the engine, also with digital electronic control is the Mk1004 Gem 2 for the Agusta A129 Mongoose anti tank/ground attack/scout helicopter for which production was initiated in 1985 after a successful development programme. Particular features include direct drive output speed at 27,000rpm and the newly emergent role of tank-busting helicopter introduces a new rating of 20 second emergency power at 1018shp in contrast with the normal 2½ minute maximum contingency, in this case at 944shp.

Smaller Engines

An elusive market for the aircraft gas turbine engine is in the lower power range below 600hp in which the piston engine is still dominant, particularly as a consequence of cost, and penetration of this field remains a continuing quest.

In 1965 a collaborative effort was undertaken with Turbomeca on the Oredon III engine to give 350hp for a weight of 175lb with a specific fuel consumption of 0.571lbs/shp/hr and an engine speed of 60,000rpm. Gearbox running was undertaken but the project did not proceed to completion. Another American collaboration was

BS347 being prepared for test at Hatfield in 1967 130lb thrust with an engine weight of 30lb.

115

pursued with Continental Aviation to licence their 250hp T65 turboshaft as the BS350. In 1966 an anglicised version, substituting a two-stage axial compressor for the single stage unit upstream of the centrifugal HP stage, was designed for 400 hp and designated the BS350/H400. In 1967 the H3 engine design of 1947 was re-examined in terms of technology update and it was calculated that using the combination of two-stage centrifugal compressor and three-stage turbine a 500hp engine could be produced with a weight of 227lbs and specific fuel consumption at 0.6lb/shp/hr. This, too, was not proceeded with.

This flurry of activity was resolved in 1967 by the company entering into a Distributor agreement with the Allison Division of General Motors. The agreement was in two parts covering sale of new engines outside North America, and establishing repair and overhaul facilities for in service support. This engine had by then established itself internationally with applications in a range of helicopters and with ratings at 317shp and 400shp. The agreement terminated with the company problems in 1971.

Two small turbojet engines are of interest. In 1967 a diminutive 130lb thrust engine weighing 30lb designated the BS347 was built and run. This was intended for a small target aircraft and similar designs were put forward by Lucas and Rover. In 1965 a 2,000lb thrust small turbofan engine, the BS 358, had been designed but only the compressor, a five-stage axial, was subsequently built and tested.

Another unit of interest was a 142hp airborne auxiliary power unit built in conjunction with the German company Klockner-Humboldt-Deutz (KHD) as the T112 and run for the first time in September 1967. This was intended as the auxiliary

RB/AR318 Turboprop sectioned display drawing.

power unit for the VFW-VAK vertical take-off strike aircraft, although this did not proceed. Subsequent development was pursued independently by KHD resulting in production of the T312 for the Tornado multi-role combat aircraft.

In June 1973, following the basic design work peak on the Gem, attention was again focussed on the lower power spectrum. A design study was launched in conjunction with Motoren Turbo Union (MTU) of Germany and Alfa Romeo of Italy, of a 600hp unit capitalising on the high pressure ratio now demonstrated as achievable in a single-stage centrifugal compressor. Two related designs were proposed in the European ESM600 and EPM600, the first a turboshaft and the second a turboprop, with a common gas generator unit and reduction gears and control units matched to the respective design application cases. In December 1973 a high pressure ratio impeller was run in a programme in conjunction with MTU but in August 1974 the joint project was placed in suspension on re-assessment of market economics.

In 1976 the concept was again pursued in the collaborative design with Alfa Romeo of the RB318 to concentrate on turboprop application at a ground level power of 600hp. In May 1977 the test compressor unit was run and in July the prototype engine ran at Hatfield.

The programme continued at a relatively low pace as the market potential was again explored. General aviation was keen to accept a contender in this field. Aviation gasoline was becoming difficult and expensive to supply, due to the effect of the fuel crisis and the general dominance of kerosene-burning aircraft. With a relatively slow-turning propeller on a turboprop engine this would be quieter than a comparable turbo-charged high performance piston engine. At 15,000ft, the practical operational height for short-haul general aviation types, the ground level 600hp turboprop would yield comparable power to the established turbo-blown piston engines at 390hp and a higher power margin at take-off and climb to that height.

In March 1979 the engine commenced hangar testing at Alfa Romeo and in December 1979 flight testing commenced as the starboard engine of a Beech King Air the port engine installation retaining its standard fitment of the competing, but assumed obsolescent, Canadian Pratt & Whitney PT6 A-20 engine.

From 1981 development of the engine continued as an Italian programme. Max. take-off power was 580hp, cruise power 330hp and specific fuel consumption was 0.582lbs/ehp/hr for an engine weight of 310lb. In June 1985, as the AR318, the engine gained Italian government and FAA flight certification. The AR318 is Italy's first indigenous turbine engine but in 1986 the project appeared once again to be in limbo.

RTM322

From 1980 the specification for a European Helicopter, EH101, awaited positive Governmental support and finance. The capacity of the aircraft suggested a three-engine installation with powers of the order of 1700hp. The Royal Navy had a positive requirement for the type as a Sea King replacement. To meet this requirement a co-operative programme was proposed with Turbomeca to design and produce as a further collaborative venture, the RTM321, initially of 1700shp at a weight of 396lb. The design was launched in April 1981.

In the event by the time the EH101 was positively launched with the intent of meeting Royal Navy and Italian naval requirements the specification had grown to a

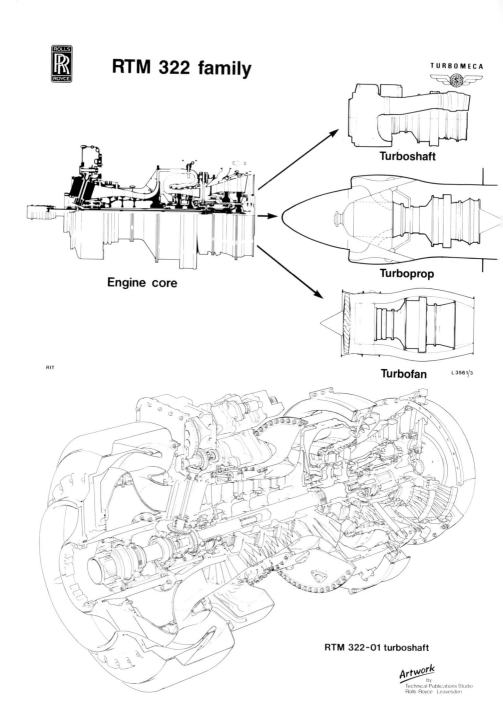

RTM 322 family

ROLLS ROYCE

TURBOMECA

Turboshaft

Turboprop

Turbofan

Engine core

RIT

L 3561/3

RTM 322-01 turboshaft

Artwork
by
Technical Publications Studio
Rolls-Royce Leavesden

118

Early run of the RTM322 on a Hatfield development test bed with all electrical/electronic recording. Test team pictured are Geoff King at controls with Ian Inwards in support. Project test engineer Terry Anderson and test engineer Peter Skakle.

Jet Propulsion, Rocket & Turbo Shaft Engine manufacture to the end of 1986			
Turbojets to 1965	Goblin	2688	
	Ghost	185	(for Comet)
	Ghost	1850	(for military)
	Gyron	12	(approx)
	Gyron Junior	100	(military; approx)
	Gyron Junior	12	(supersonic research)
Rockets to 1960	Sprite	12	(approx)
	Supersprite	166	
	Spectre	65	
Turboshafts at year end 1986	Gnome	2200	
	Gem	1000	
	RTM322	8	(development)

requirement for 2100shp engines and the design was revised as the RTM322. The basic engine features a Turbomeca designed three-stage axial compressor, with variable inlet guide vanes and first stage stators, on a common shaft with a high pressure stage centrifugal compressor giving an overall 14 to 1 pressure ratio, and driven by a two-stage turbine with combustion in a reverse-flow annular chamber. Output power is from a further two-stage turbine with forward drive to an aircraft-provisioned gearbox. The engine, whilst similar in concept to the Gem, is considerably simpler with a single gas generator rotor and only two bearing chambers.

The gas generator first ran in December 1984 and the complete basic engine in February 1985. Eight bench engines were running in the development programme by December 1985 at which time a flight clearance test was completed and the first two flight engines built. Powers to 2,300shp had been achieved. Flight trials commenced on 14 June 1986 in a Sikorsky S70C, this helicopter type being a prime example a potential application as a result of increasing US military interest in the engine.

Chapter 13
CONCLUSION

This account has considered in some depth the span of sixty years of activity.from 1926, and in the first generation of the history considered, it followed the classic progression of an organisation in consistent growth under the control of a dedicated founding group, paternalistic in style of management, and motivated by the excitement of the growth of a new industry. These years saw the creation of the light aircraft movement, record breaking, and the birth of airline travel, with all of which de Havillands had a major role. In Halford's Napier activities there was a strong

H R H The Queen Mother being shown the Goblin and other engine exhibits by John Cunningham at the Mosquito Aircraft Museum at Salisbury Hall near St. Albans in May 1984 when a major extension was dedicated.

Assembly Shop personnel and some supporting staff and management on the occasion of the completion of the 2000th Gnome in August 1982.

The RTM322 powered Sikorsky S70C and Gem powered Agusta A129 Mongoose demonstrated at Leavesden.in Autumn 1986.

Engine design genealogy — Gipsy to Gem

		PISTON	JET	TURBOSHAFT	ROCKET	AUXILIARY	NON-AVIATION ACTIVITIES
1900's	08	DH IRIS					
1920's	27	GIPSY 'R'			DE HAVILLAND		
		GIPSY I					
	28	GHOST					
	29	GIPSY II					
1930's	30	GIPSY III					
	32	GIPSY MAJOR					
	33	GIPSY SIX					
	34	GIPSY SIX 'R'					
	37	GIPSY TWELVE					
	38	GIPSY MINOR					
1940's	40	MAJOR 30				GIPSY SIX A. G. P. 4 CYL A. G. P.	
	41						
	42						
	43	MAJOR 50					
	44	QUEEN 30					
	45	QUEEN 70					
	46	MAJOR 10	GOBLIN			CABIN SUPERCHARGER (For 'Comet')	Campbell's 'Bluebird' with GOBLIN
	47		GHOST I				
	48			H3 PROTOTYPE			
	49		GHOST 50		SPRITE		
1950's	51						Ship trials with 'Lucy Ashton'
	52		GYRON I		SUPER SPRITE		Cobb's 'Crusader' with GHOST
	53		GYRON JUNIOR		SPECTRE		N. P. G. Gas Cooled Reactor equipment
	54		GYRON 2			PEROXIDE A. P. U. PEROXIDE STARTER	
	55						
	56	MAJOR 215					D.H./Erlich 125cc Racing Motorcycle
	57						& 150cc Boost Port 2 stroke
	58	MAJOR 215 Turboblown		GNOME	COUPLED SPECTRE		
	59						
1960's	60	BRISTOL SIDDELEY		COUPLED GNOME GNOME H1400 GNOME H1800		T112 PROTOTYPE	'WATER GIPSY' Outboard motor 'AUTO VISTA' forecourt pumps
	61						
	62						
	65		BS347 PROTOTYPE	BS360			
	66						
	67						
	69				continues as ROLLS-ROYCE LIMITED		
1970's	75			GEM 2 GNOME H1400-1T RB318			
	76						
	77						
1980's	80			RTM321 GEM60 RTM322			
	81						
	85						

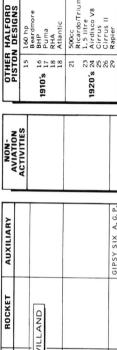

OTHER HALFORD PISTON DESIGNS		
1910's	15	160 hp
	16	Beardmore
	17	BHP
	18	Puma
	18	RHA
	18	Atlantic
1920's	21	500cc
	21	Ricardo/Triumph
	23	1.5 litre
	24	Airdisco V8
	25	Cirrus
	26	Cirrus II
	29	Rapier
1930's	32	Javelin
	34	Dagger
	37	Sabre

L5026

involvement in the high powered piston engine for military aircraft and, with the subsequent development of the gas turbine jet propulsion engine, this paved the way for the formation of the de Havilland Engine Company and major contributions to the design and application of jet propulsion engines, initially in their military application and subsequently in the creation of civil transport applications. The latter years of this phase were associated with the first of the supersonic engine designs and the application of rocket engine technology to the propulsion of manned aircraft.

In the latter thirty years the era of the consolidation of the aircraft and the engine companies coincided with, and related to, the accelerating rate of change in overall technology. The Leavesden organisation reverted to involvement in a particular sector of propulsion. That of the design, development, and manufacture of small gas turbines, primarily of the turboshaft type, for the growing worldwide helicopter market. This complementing the work of other parts of the national organisation of the Rolls-Royce company and its international market affiliations.

The present organisation based at Leavesden has its roots firmly founded in the prior sixty years in terms of the development of its products, its facilities, and its people, perpetuating the positive virtues of its foundation and combining all lessons learnt, and the practices and technology of the overall company, into what is appreciated as the Leavesden spirit.

Engineering equipment, manufacturing machines and facilities

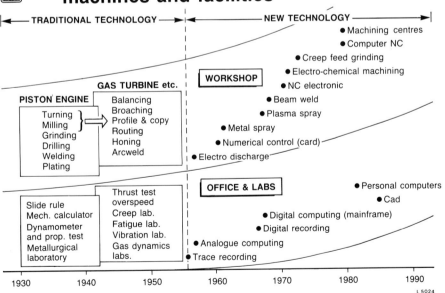

125

Company Sites and personnel — Gipsy to Gem

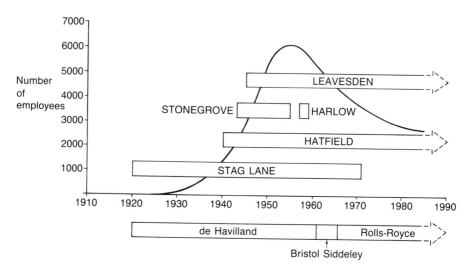

Products and output — Gipsy to Gem

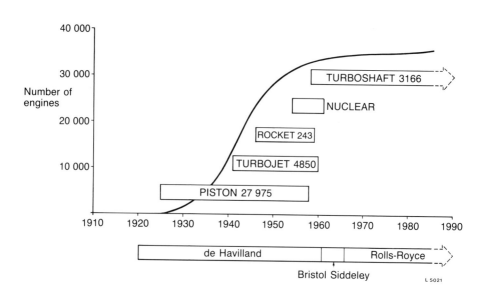